The New Supervisor's Workbook

Success in the First Year of Supervision

Tyra P. Sellers
TP Sellers, LLC

and

Linda A. LeBlanc
LeBlanc Behavioral Consulting

KeyPress Publishing

© 2022 KeyPress Publishing
930 South Harbor City Blvd., Melbourne, FL 32901

KeyPress
Publishing

Authors: Tyra Sellers & Linda LeBlanc

The New Supervisor's Workbook: Success in the First Year of Supervision

Published by: KeyPress Publishing
Cover design: Jana Burtner
Text design: Jana Burtner
Illustration: Jana Burtner
Production Coordinator: Shauna Costello

ISBN 978-1-7377574-2-9

Distributed by:
ABA Technologies, Inc.
930 South Harbor City Blvd, Suite 402
Melbourne, FL 32901
Telephone: 321-222-6822
www.abatechnologies.com

KeyPress Publishing books are available at a special discount for bulk purchases by corporations, institutions, and other organizations. For more information, please call 321-222-6822 or email keypress@abatechnologies.com.

Acknowledgments

We would like to acknowledge Scott LaPorta, Erin O'Brien, Janet Lund, Francine Holguin, Dana Meller, Jayme Mews, Audrey Hoffman, Kristine Rodriguez, who reviewed early drafts of the book and provided invaluable feedback.

Contents

I. Introduction   **6**

II. Getting Ready   **10**

III. Month-to-Month Guides: The Early Months   **42**

     a. Month 1: Planning Logistics and Building Relationships 44

     b. Month 2: Assessing and Self-Assessing 71

     c. Month 3: Curricular Roadmap and Competencies 85

IV. Month-to-Month Guides: The Individualized Plan   **98**

     a. Month 4 99

     b. Month 5 102

     c. Month 6 105

     d. Month 7 113

     e. Month 8 116

     f. Month 9 122

     g. Month 10 126

     h. Month 11 129

     i. Month 12: Wrapping Up Consultation 132

V. Specific Skills   **149**

     a. Compassionate Care and Therapeutic Relationships 151

     b. Enhancing Learning:
         Self-Monitoring, Describing, and Asking Meaningful Questions 155

     c. Evaluating Effects of Supervision 159

     d. Feedback and Difficult Conversations 163

     e. Ongoing Monitoring and Performance Management 168

    f. Organizational Skills and Time Management 172

    g. Problem-Solving and Decision Making 175

    h. Public Speaking and Professional Presentations. 181

    i. Scope Of Competence 186

    j. Self-Care 190

    k. Teaching Effectively Using Behavioral Skills Training (BST) 193

VI. References   197

Introduction

Congratulations on your recent success in becoming a Board-Certified Behavior Analyst® (BCBA®)! You are now part of an ever-growing community of BCBAs. Based on the steep growth trajectory in our profession, the percentage of BCBAs considered new (i.e., certified in the last five years, just like you) is increasing and will continue to make up well over half of all BCBAs (Behavior Analyst Certification board, n.d.a). One of the most important responsibilities of a BCBA is to supervise others who are practicing as a Registered Behavior Technician® (RBT®) or Board-Certified Assistant Behavior Analyst® (BCaBA®), and those who are pursuing certification (i.e., trainees) as you have just done. You have completed coursework and supervised fieldwork experience hours. Now it is your turn to master the art of meaningful and effective supervision. We are so excited to support you, in conjunction with your Consulting Supervisor (CS) on this supervisory journey!

Beginning January 1, 2022, the Behavior Analyst Certification Board® (BACB®, May, 2021b) instituted a new requirement for oversight of the supervisory efforts of newly certified BCBAs like you. Any BCBA providing supervision to trainees accruing fieldwork experience toward certification in their first-year post certification must have oversight of that supervision by a qualified CS (i.e., a BCBA for at least five years and in good standing). The overarching purpose of the consultation is to learn from a more experienced supervisor what to do as a supervisor, when and how to do it, and why

it is important to do these things with all your supervisees and trainees.

The BCBA and their CS must meet every month for guidance on effective supervision practices (BACB, May, 2021b). This new requirement presents a tremendous opportunity for you to fully embrace the value and power of meaningful and effective supervision as laid out by LeBlanc, Sellers et al. (2020). As a new supervisor, you will have support and guidance to help you fully realize your valuable role as a supervisor. The BACB also provides general guidance about the structure of the consultation you will be receiving (BACB, May, 2021b). For example, you must meet with your CS for at least one hour per month until you have been certified for at least one year. The consultation meeting must be synchronous, one-on-one (online meetings are permitted), and documentation needs to be completed for each meeting.

The purpose of consultation is to provide you with guidance and professional development for facilitating high-quality supervision of trainees (BACB, May, 2021b). That is, your CS is NOT intended to provide ongoing supervision related to your general practice of behavior analysis. The focus of the consultation should be supervision, training, and performance management. In other words, the content you and your CS cover should not be based on the full BACB Task List 5th ed. (BACB, 2017) and instead it should incorporate the content outlined in the Supervision Curriculum Outline 2.0 (BACB, 2018). Although the BACB requirement is in effect for trainees pursuing fieldwork, you will find much of the content of this year of consultation is also useful for your supervision of RBTs and BCaBAs.

These requirements established by the BACB represent the minimum requirements for consulting support within the first year of certification. However, most newly certified BCBAs will need more than the bare minimum of consultation to succeed. You'll need a structured plan for how to make the most of that precious hour per month of consultation. You'll benefit from taking a structured approach to leveraging the support of other supervisors or managers and your peers. Finally, you may need some improvements or guidance on your supervision of RBTs and BCaBAs.

This workbook is designed to do all of that! Use this resource during your first-year, post-certification providing BACB-required supervision to trainees during their independent fieldwork experience. Your experience may be enhanced if your CS simultaneously uses the companion workbook *The First Year of Supervision: The Consulting Supervisor's Guide*. If your CS does not use the companion workbook, this guide will still benefit you by providing structure and facilitating a planful approach to your first year of supervisory activities for trainees.

The goal is to increase the likelihood of three outcomes:

1. a successful supervisory relationship for you and your trainee(s),
2. trainee(s) who are likely to become successful supervisors, and
3. increased professional growth for you during this exciting, but stressful first year of supervisory practices.

The self-reflection and planning activities provided in this workbook will also positively impact the supervision you provide to RBTs and BCaBAs.

This workbook does not focus on *"the what"* of supervision (i.e., teaching behavior- analytic content to your trainees). This workbook does not outline the behavior-analytic content that you should cover with your trainees. You should already be well positioned to do that based on your academic coursework. If you do not feel fully prepared to teach the behavior-analytic content, you might use the self-assessment in LeBlanc, Sellers et al. (2020) to directly assess your areas of confidence or concern. That text and a comprehensive behavior-analysis text such as Cooper et al. (2020) can help you strengthen areas where you feel this is needed.

This workbook focuses on the *"how"* of supervision. Becoming a supervisor to trainees is a big responsibility. You are responsible for the outcomes of your trainee's clients and for developing your trainee's clinical application skills *and* their supervisory skills. This is a tall order, but the good news is that you will have the support of your CS and this workbook to help you meet the challenge. This workbook focuses on ensuring that you engage in and address the critical, often overlooked, and untaught tasks of successful supervision in a structured way. In other words, this workbook and activities will support you in developing your own supervisory skills and teaching those skills to your trainees and supervisees. In addition, this workbook will help you maximize the time you have with your CS. You may also find it useful to refer to LeBlanc, Sellers et al., (2020); Sellers, Valentino et al., (2016); Sellers, Alai-Rosales et al., (2016) for additional support.

Even if you are not a brand-new supervisor, this workbook can still serve as a valuable resource to guide your efforts! Even if you are already supervising trainees (or others), this guidebook can be used to help you evaluate and refine your supervisory practices. You could choose to start using the book with a brand-new trainee and compare it to your practices and outcomes with your past or other concurrent trainees. This will allow you to take a structured approach to evaluating your supervisory practices, particularly related to focusing on the critical skills and activities that will position your trainees to transition into successful, independent practitioners. Alternatively, you could review the content and simply pick and choose the activities and areas of focus that you have specifically identified for growth.

This workbook is broken into five main sections:

1. pre-supervision activities to get you ready to supervise,

2. month-to-month guides for Months 1, 2, and 3 to ensure that you build a strong foundation,

3. month-to-month templates for Month 4 through Month 11 to facilitate you and your CS take an individualized approach to designing content that will maximize your growth,

4. a wrap-up section that includes the content for Month 12 and tips for concluding the consultation relationship, and

5. a skills-specific section with additional topics and resources that can be used to build the content for those latter months.

The pre-supervision activities are best completed in advance of supervising others and in advance of beginning the consultation relationship with your CS. Hopefully, you picked up this book a few months before you'll start supervising trainees. This will give you some time to engage in some self-reflection and planning activities that will set you up for success. If you are just finding this book at the same time you have started supervising, that's okay, too. You can still go through the pre-supervision activities, a little bit at a time, over the course of your first few months and revisit them anytime you need.

In the section covering the content for the early months (i.e., Month 1 through 3), each month is comprised of pre-meeting reflection and preparation activities, meetings activities, and follow-up activities to provide structure to the supervision you are providing to your trainees, and to maximize the consultation you are receiving from your CS. You'll not only get guidance on how to maximize the tasks you can do independently and with your CS to positively impact your supervisory practices, but we have also included tips for activities you might consider completing with your colleagues, peers, or community of practice; (don't fret, we will talk more about this in a bit). For some topics we have also included discussion guides that you can use to help provide structure to conversations with your supervisees and trainees.

The first three months are laid out for you and your CS in an order that will help you start your supervisory relationship and manage your stress. These months will assist you in managing the many logistics associated with fieldwork experience while helping you build a solid foundation for your supervisory relationship. You will focus on developing basic, foundational skills such as skills assessment, values identification, collaborative goal setting, creating a feedback-rich environment, developing structured agendas, and running effective and enjoyable meetings. Months 4 through 11 are presented in template format, allowing you and your CS to build a tailored 8-month plan using the information from your self-assessment, their assessment of your skills, your goals, and content from the available topics in the workbook. The 8-month plan that you create should be considered a flexible path that may need to be adjusted based on your needs and the needs of your trainees. The last section includes content for Month 12 and strategies for wrapping up your time with your CS with an eye toward planning your ongoing professional development and self-care for career longevity and developing a plan for success with your continued supervisory practices. We want you in this profession for the long haul, and we don't want to leave that up to chance.

Getting Ready

Preparation and planning are critical to success in supervision. The activities in this section will set you on a path for success in your supervisory practices and your continued professional growth. This is especially true if you have or have had limited access to mentors, advisors, and supervisors. Minimally, you will have one monthly meeting with your CS to support your activities with your supervisees and trainees, in addition to all your other work and life requirements. Taking an active approach to planning *before* you even start meeting with your CS and trainees will allow you to maximize your time and efforts, minimize additional stressors, and increase the chances of positively developing your supervisory skills to the benefit of your trainees, supervisees, and clients.

The best-case scenario has you starting this section *before* you begin providing supervision to trainees and *before* you begin meeting with your CS. Why? You'll maximize everyone's time if you begin by critically assessing your own skills, identifying goals that you can share with your CS, identifying resources to support you, and getting yourself organized in advance of your limited time with your CS and trainees.

The four main activities you'll work on in this section are:

1. reflecting & self-assessing,
2. identifying draft goals for yourself,
3. identifying supports and resources, and
4. managing the logistics of supervision.

The last activity will help prepare you for your first meeting with your CS. The first meeting is a "pre-meeting" as it should occur before you begin your monthly CS and trainee meetings. Let's get started!

It is likely that you already have a CS, or will be assigned one through your employer, and that's great. However, you might have to identify a CS on your own and might not know where to start. If that is the case, here are some tips for identifying one: 1) ask for recommendations from trusted colleagues, past supervisor(s), or professors, 2) contact your state or regional ABAI affiliated chapter, 3) contact presenters or workshop providers, and 4) search the BACB Certificant Registry for a BCBA willing to provide supervision. You might have to be persistent in reaching out to several people and sending out follow-up emails. We have provided more structured tips for identifying a CS in Appendix A. If you don't have a CS just yet, don't stop reading here while you identify one. Move forward with the Getting Ready activities while you are working to identify a CS. You and your CS will be glad you did!

Reflection and Self-Assessment

To be a competent, independent clinician and supervisor, you must be a self-directed active learner, continually evaluating and adding to your repertoires in a purposeful manner. Keep in mind that we are focusing on skills related to successful supervision, not general behavior-analytic clinical skills (e.g., client assessment, intervention programming). The first step in this lifelong process is to self-reflect, which for our purposes, involves remembering and describing your past experiences and responses, objectively noticing your current behavior, and evaluating the degree to which your past experiences have shaped your current behavior. Self-reflecting on your experiences as a supervisee can help you identify and optimize your skills, as well as help you avoid imitating non-optimal or deficient exemplars. Self-reflection can also facilitate the identification and description of your goals and values.

Generally speaking, goals are discrete, can be objectively measured and evaluated, and are meant to be completed once a specific outcome has been realized (Chase, 2013). *Values* are described as the things that are most important to you in life or in a specific area of life, such as supervision. Values can never be fully achieved, but they can direct your behavior (Chase, 2013). For example, I may have a goal that 100% of my trainees pass the BACB exam the first time, and an overarching value of supporting the success of others. See chapter 3 in LeBlanc, Sellers et al. (2020) to learn more about the benefits of, and strategies for, engaging in self-reflection related to supervisory repertoires.

The second step in being a self-directed learner is to engage in self-assessment. Doing so involves regularly evaluating your skills to identify your relative strengths and areas in need of improvement. As a newly certified BCBA, you have met the minimum level of competence to practice independently and supervise RBTs and BCaBAs. However, there will be certain areas from the Task List where your skills are more fluent and others where you must continue learning and improving. Moreover, there are likely supervisory skills that you have not yet mastered (e.g., providing effective feedback, teaching feedback delivery and reception, tacting your decision-making processes, engaging in and teaching structured problem-solving) that are critical to building an effective supervisory repertoire.

Activity 1: Self-Reflection

Schedule 30-60 minutes in your calendar for this reflection activity. Select a time that is likely to be uninterrupted and a location where you will be comfortable and focused. For example, you might go to a café or find a spot under a shady tree. Also, select a time when you have the energy to engage in deep reflection about your past supervisory experiences. It's a good idea to have a pen or pencil along with this workbook as you should jot down notes and follow-up actions. Reflect on the following questions and use the space provided to record your thoughts (if you need more space, use the notes pages at the end of the Getting Ready section).

1. Who has served as a supervisor or mentor for you throughout your life? _____

_____

2. What did these supervisors do that you really liked? What did they do that made you feel successful or supported? How did they create an environment of learning? _____

_____

    a. What did you most value from each experience? _____

    _____

    b. Can you identify any of those behaviors in your own supervisory behavior? _____

    _____

3. What did these supervisors do that you did not like? What did they do that made you feel unsuccessful or unsupported? What did they do that presented barriers to your learning? _____

_____

    a. Can you identify any of those behaviors in your own supervisory behavior? _____

    _____

4. Have you ever expressly told a past supervisor what you liked about the supervisory experience with them? If not, consider calendaring some time to send a thank-you email or note. _____

_____

5. What are the top 2-3 things you value about providing supervision? Maybe it's consumer protection, establishing a passion for life-long learning in others, or the health and success of the profession. Identifying and behaving toward your core values for supervision can help you make decisions and sustain your supervisory practices even when things are difficult. _____

_____

_____

Activity 2: Self-Assessment

Just like you did for the self-reflection activities, schedule time (30-90 minutes) to complete the self-assessment activities. Be honest in your self-assessment and remember that you have more access to information about your performance and skills than anyone else does. Start by spending a few minutes thinking about these two questions:

1. Which areas of my supervisory skills need the most work, development, or support? _____

_____

2. Which areas of my supervisory skills need the least work, development, or support because they are already strong? _____

_____

Once you have spent a few minutes thinking about those general questions, move on to completing the Self-Assessment of Foundational Supervision Skills. We recommend the following approach:

1. review the items in the self-assessment,

2. spend a few minutes thinking about each one and just noticing your initial responses,

3. review the items with a past supervisor, mentor, advisor, or close colleague and ask them their thoughts about your relative strengths and areas for improvement, and

4. go back and complete the self-assessment.

Instructions: Rate each of the following supervision and mentorship skills as: 3) proficient, 2) developing, 1) not yet acquired. Mark an asterisk (*) if your repertoire for the skill includes some problematic history and performance aspects (e.g., history of receiving harsh feedback and you sometimes behave the same way when giving feedback).

1. Score 3 for proficient if you perform the skill accurately and consistently with little preparation, effort, and only minimal distractors.

2. Score 2 for developing if you are not yet able to perform the skill consistently and accurately, even under optimal conditions.

3. Score 1 for not yet acquired if you have not yet had the opportunity to learn the skill.

Specific Foundational Supervision Skill	Score

BACB Supervision Requirements

1. Describe basic requirements (e.g., frequency of supervision, relevant activities, acceptable modalities, use of group supervision).
2. Name, describe purpose and how to use, and access required documents and forms.
3. Describe, create, use, and teach others how to use documentation systems.
4. Develop a contract and review the contract with a supervisee using an informed consent approach.

TOTAL:

Purpose of Supervision

1. Describe the purpose for implementing behavior-analytic supervision (e.g., the benefits and desired outcomes).
2. Describe the potential risks of ineffective supervision (e.g., poor client outcomes, poor supervisee performance).

TOTAL:

Structuring Supervision

1. Develop a positive rapport.
2. Schedule and run effective meetings based on LeBlanc & Nosik (2019) checklist.
3. Establish clear performance expectations for the trainee and supervisee.
4. Conduct assessments of the supervisee or trainee.
5. Select supervision goals based on an assessment to improve relevant skills (BACB Task List based and ethics).

TOTAL:

Training and Performance Management

1. Explain the purpose of feedback and discuss preferences for trainee to receive and give feedback.
2. Use Behavior Skills Training (BST) in teaching supervisees and trainees.
3. Train personnel to competently perform assessment and intervention procedures.
4. Use performance monitoring, feedback, and reinforcement systems.
5. Use a functional assessment approach (e.g., performance diagnostics) and tools (Performance Diagnostic Checklist-Human Services; PDC-HS) to identify variables affecting personnel performance.
6. Use function-based strategies to improve personnel performance.

TOTAL:

(Continues on next page)

Specific Foundational Supervision Skill	Score
Evaluating the Effects of Supervision	
1. Solicit, review, and respond to feedback from supervises, trainees, and others.	
2. Evaluate the effects of supervision (e.g., on client outcomes, on supervisee repertoires).	
3. Implement changes when needed.	
TOTAL:	
Monitoring and Managing Stress and Wellness	
1. Monitor your own stress levels and detect the effects of stress on your supervisory skills and on others.	
2. Engage in appropriate self-care strategies to manage stress (i.e., identify alternative behaviors when you notice you are impacted by stress).	
3. Teach supervisees and trainees to monitor their stress levels and detect effects on others.	
4. Teach supervisees and trainees to engage in appropriate self-care strategies to manage stress.	
TOTAL:	

Review your completed self-assessment, paying close attention to individual skills with a 1 or an asterisk, and skill areas with the lowest overall totals. These are areas to prioritize for discussion with your CS and target for growth. Be prepared to review and discuss the results with your CS over the first few meetings. Think about some examples that you use to illustrate why you elected to give a skill a specific score. Don't be surprised if your CS engages you in discussion or activities to evaluate the skills you scored as fluent. A skilled supervisor will work to validate their supervisee's self-assessment scores, as the result provides valuable information about the accuracy of the supervisee's self-observation and evaluation skills.

Throughout your first year, and with guidance from your CS, you may wish to complete in-depth, self-assessments in a particular area you identify for growth. We include an advanced self-assessment that you and your CS will implement later. Your CS may ask you to complete the entire self-assessment at once, or may break it up, asking you to complete relevant skills areas across two or more months. We also provide additional skills assessments for each topic covered in the Specific Skills that included assessment and skills-building strategies for you and your trainees. You can also use the Supervision Training Curriculum Outline (2.0) (BACB, 2018) as a self-assessment and make notes about areas in which you feel you might need the most support from your CS. Finally, the book by LeBlanc, Sellers et al. (2020) has a series of in-depth, skill-specific assessments across several chapters. For each chapter, the assessment is dedicated to the content of that chapter (e.g., cultural responsiveness, organization and time management, problem-solving, interpersonal communication skills). You may wish to complete one or more of these specific self-assessments over the next several months with the support of your CS.

Now that you have completed the reflection and self-assessment activities, let's move on to goal identification. You want to accomplish some things during this important and formative year of supervision! Taking this time to prepare for your first few meetings with your CS will allow you to maximize the time you have with them. Share the results of your self-assessment with your CS before or during your first meeting so that they can review the results and help you formulate and revise your goals in the coming months.

Taking time to self-reflect, beginning to identify your values, and self-assessing your skills and needs related to supervisory practices is critical. Let's put that time to good use by distilling the information into goals. These goals are preliminary—you'll review them with your CS in your first few meetings and they should continue to evolve over the course of your consultation.

Activity 3: Identifying Goals for Yourself

Review your notes and results from your self-reflection and self-assessment and use that information to answer the following foundational questions:

1. What kind of supervisor do you want to be? _____

_____

_____

2. What overarching impacts or outcomes do you want for yourself from your supervisory relationships? For your supervisees? _____

_____

_____

3. What do you want from your CS? _____

_____

_____

Use the results from your reflection and self-assessment activities and the questions above to complete the Initial Goal Planning Activity on the following page to draft 2-4 goals for yourself that you will share with your CS. Focus on goals related to foundational skills (i.e., mastering the skill will facilitate acquisition of other skills) and areas that will have an immediate positive impact as you begin your supervisory practices. Some of the goals may be addressed directly in your meetings with your CS (e.g., complicated skills that are unlikely to be mastered without explicit instruction or coaching and feedback). Other goals will be more appropriate for you to work on independently, periodically reviewing your progress with your CS. For example, working on organizational skills is important, but you might be able to address that goal independently through accessing resources, self-management, and reporting to your CS. On the other hand, if you have difficulty with critical, foundational skills such as providing effective feedback or having difficult conversations, you are unlikely to move the needle in a positive direction without some explicit instruction, modeling, practice, and feedback from your CS.

Be as specific as possible in writing your draft goals. Ask yourself "What will this look like, how will I know when I have made progress, and how will improvements positively impact my trainees?" For example, instead of writing: "Get better at building rapport" consider something more specific, such as, "Develop five, open-ended questions aimed at getting to know the trainee and build fluency in asking them, and related follow-up questions." So, focus on trying to outline the exact behavior you would like to exhibit more or less of. Consider including how and when you plan on engaging in the behavior in your goal, although this specific information may be added as you revise the goals with your CS. If you have a difficult time making your draft goals more precise, that's okay—that's what your CS is for!

You will work with your CS to revise the goals, and likely add in a few more, during your first few meetings. You will revisit these goals each month to determine progress and you will add new goals over the coming months. So, don't try to identify all your needs right away; just focus on the most pressing needs that will allow you to start strong with your trainees.

Draft Goals
....

Draft Goal 1: _____

_____

_____

Draft Goal 2: _____

_____

_____

Draft Goal 3: _____

_____

_____

Draft Goal 4: _____

_____

_____

Supports and Resources

Figuring out all your new responsibilities can be overwhelming, and the demands on your time are likely to increase throughout your first year. Taking some time to think about and identify the resources you have, and those you'd like to get or develop, will prove invaluable as needs arise. Review the different categories below and then complete the My Supports activity.

- **You**. You are one of your most powerful, available, and renewable resources. In the coming months you will have many successes to celebrate, and you may also have to pull yourself through some difficult situations and keep yourself motivated. You can use the information you identified in the previous activities about your values, strengths, and goals to help keep yourself motivated. Self-management can be a useful tool that can help you take a structured approach to being a lifelong learner. Self-management involves self-monitoring (i.e., observing and recording your own performance), self-assessing, goal setting, implementing goals, and evaluating your progress and outcomes (Murphy & Ensher, 2001). For more self-management information and activities see Chapter 6 in the book by LeBlanc, Sellers et al. (2020).

- **Your CS.** Obviously, your CS will be an invaluable resource during this first year of supervision. It is critical that you both work to create a collaborative relationship that focuses on addressing your supervisory skills rather than your basic behavior-analytic skills. Put effort into developing a trusting relationship where you feel comfortable asking difficult questions and receiving critical feedback from your CS. Spend some time thinking about how you can identify if your CS shares your core values and have open conversations in the first few meetings to help establish a strong foundation. See LeBlanc, Sellers et al. (2020) for more specific guidance and activities on how to build a strong supervisory relationship.

- **Workplace Supervisors, Managers, & Leaders.** In addition to your CS, you likely have other leaders in your workplace who can be great resources for you. Your direct supervisor or manager can help with day-to-day issues, and they can also help you with your specific goals and how to address difficult situations with your trainees. Whereas your CS can support you to identify possible/actual problems and related solutions, the leaders in your workplace will know more about the parameters of performance management and available resources in your environment. It may also be worthwhile to share your specific goals with them and make time in your regular meetings to debrief them on your progress and any issues with your trainees that may be on the horizon.

- **Peers, Colleagues & Community of Practice.** Your peers and colleagues are individuals who are in the same or similar position as you and work in a similar context or setting. They are wonderful resources for sharing ideas and discussing how things are going with your respective trainees. Communities of practice (CoPs) are groups of people who have shared values and goals and are committed to learning in the service of those values and meeting those goals (Wenger & Snyder, 2000). A CoP can be made up of your peers who work at the same organization as you, as well as those who work in similar contexts but in different organizations. Consider creating a CoP of other new supervisors (e.g., those in their first few years of delivering supervision). Schedule regular meetings (e.g., monthly) together for support and idea sharing. These meetings can be a source of motivation during difficult times, as well as a platform to practice skills and celebrate successes. Meeting with your peers also increases the number of exemplars and perspectives that you each contact, and may provide a brave space for addressing difficult topics, thereby broadening the learning occurring in the meetings with your CS.

- **Published Resources.** Now is a good time to begin building and organizing your cache of resources to use during supervision. Consider making two categories: 1) things that you want to use with your trainees (e.g., feedback forms, journal articles, video examples, agendas, activities, case scenarios, the current BACB Task List) and 2) resources that can help you as a supervisor. See the "Supervisor's Starter Resource List" at the end of this section to get started building your resources.

Activity 4: Identifying Supports & Resources

Having access to resources is as critical to being a successful supervisor as it is for being a successful clinician. Being part of the profession of applied behavior analysis means that you can benefit from the scholarly work of other behavior analysts. You will also find valuable resources outside of the ABA profession (e.g., psychology, social work, counseling). Listing out your available resources now will allow you to maximize using them when relevant and may make you feel more comfortable as you embark on this crucial endeavor of developing your supervisory repertoires. This activity will also help you identify areas where you need to add more resources, and your CS can help with that. Start by completing the Supervisor Resources Table on the following page.

In this activity you will identify resources, but more importantly, in some categories, you'll identify actions you can commit to and take that will maximize your use of these resources. You'll also identify other resources that you would like to get access to and set due dates for acquiring them. Consider reviewing the Supervisor's Starter Resource List, Appendix B, for ideas. It's okay if this activity feels overwhelming; take a breath. The goal is not to build a complete library of all available resources. The goal is simply to get started in an organized manner. You will add to your resource list over time, but getting things well organized now will make it easier for you to find, identify holes, and add to your resources throughout your career.

Supervisor Resources Table

YOU	Your Consulting Supervisor	Other Supervisors, Managers, & Leaders	Peers, Colleagues, & Community of Support	Other Resources
List how you will use yourself as a resource (e.g., schedule 15 min weekly to reflect on your successes, daily/weekly journal, structured self-management, structured self-care goals).	List how you will actively work to create an open and collaborative relationship with your CS (e.g., have a conversation about each of your values, commit to being open to each other's mistakes and support).	List the names of some individuals you will rely on as resources for supervisory practices and when you will meet with them.	List the names of some peers and colleagues with whom you can develop a community of practice focusing on supervisory practices and when you will meet with them.	List a few resources that you do not yet have and a due date for getting them.

Now that you have completed the table, you have a few more tasks. First, gather up the supervision-relevant resources (e.g., books, articles, podcasts, videos, templates) you have collected throughout your coursework, fieldwork activities, and any other contexts. Next, spend a few minutes organizing them in logical categories and house them in an easy-to-access location. Consider when and how you will use these resources when deciding on a location for storing them. For example, if there are materials you will likely use in meetings or activities with your trainees and supervisees in the field (e.g., during in-home sessions, in the community), consider storing them on a cloud-based storage system you can access on your smartphone, tablet, or laptop. With physical materials, like books, if you think you'll reference them in applied settings, it can be helpful to have a book bag that travels with you; alternatively, you could purchase an electronic version of the book. Finally, go back through your list, identify the resources you do not yet have (e.g., use a highlighter), prioritize them (e.g., place a number next to the item starting with 1 for most important), and set a due date for getting them. Consider setting up alerts through your favorite journals or search engine to make it easy to remain up to date on new articles and scientific findings.

The expectation is not that you read or re-read your resources all at once to prepare for supervision, or that you read each new resource as soon as you get it. Instead, cultivate the healthy habit of making regular contact with the resources for relatively brief periods of time. For example, add a recurring event on your calendar for 20 or 30 minutes every week or every other week to explore a new resource or revisit a familiar resource. You can also share the workload by splitting up resources across your peers in your CoP group. Each person can be responsible for reviewing a resource and creating a brief outline of the most important or useful information and sharing it with the group. We do highly recommend getting and reviewing the articles from the 2016 special section on supervision in Behavior Analysis in Practice, as they provide useful strategies and include helpful resources in the appendices. Another resource that we highly recommend is the LeBlanc, Sellers et al. (2020) supervision and mentorship book. Many of the chapters provide additional information, activities, and resources directly related to the topics covered in the workbook pair.

If you do not yet have the relevant BACB resources, prioritize them and calendar some time to get very familiar with them. It is important that you remain up to date about changes to requirements and documents from the BACB, so pay attention to announcements and newsletters, and consider creating a recurring quarterly calendar event to download any documents from the website to ensure you have the most current. There is a specific section on BACB resources in the Supervisor's Starter Resource List at the end of this section.

Hopefully, creating your list and organizing your materials will help you breathe a small sigh of relief. Being able to easily access relevant resources can save you and your trainee's time and can reduce stress. In addition, it is great to model accessing resources for your trainees. Finally, when building your CoP, you can share your list and resources to help support your colleagues and you will quickly be able to identify if others have resources that you would like to add to your cache.

The last part of getting ready is to start thinking about some of the logistics around meeting with your CS and around meeting with your trainees. Managing the details can make or break you, and you are in charge of those details! Your success will depend on how well you plan and execute the logistics associated with your activities with your CS and with each of your trainees and RBT and BCaBA supervisees! There are initial logistics and ongoing logistics for each of these relationships. Use Activity 5 to ensure that you have thought through the details for each. Again, it is not necessary, nor possible, to have all the logistics figured out ahead of time. However, spending a little bit of time thinking about them will expedite getting the ball rolling. In addition, having some ideas and options for your CS and your trainees demonstrates that you are prepared and value their time.

Activity 5: The Logistics

You will need to coordinate some aspects directly with your CS in a pre-meeting, but it is good to have some ideas ahead of time. Think about each of the following items prior to that meeting.

- Day/time of monthly meeting—Be prepared with a few good options; consider meeting early in the month so that you have ample time to implement any assigned tasks. Select a time of day suited to alert, engaged participation.
- Location of meeting—in-person, video conference, back-up plans.
- File storage and sharing—Attend to any restrictions/requirements from your employer/organization.

The logistics considerations for meeting with and managing your trainees are similar, but you need to have those more fleshed out as there are some aspects that you will directly control. Importantly, you'll need to be fluent with all the BACB requirements for supervision (e.g., qualification requirements, requirements for supervision hours each period based on hours accrued, allowable use of group supervision, acceptable fieldwork activities, documentation). A lack of familiarity with the BACB requirements can have a serious negative impact (e.g., denying all or some of their fieldwork hours) on your trainees if the BACB determines that requirements were not met. In fact, standard 4.01 of the Ethics Code for Behavior Analysts (BACB, 2020, p. 15) states: "Behavior analysts are knowledgeable about and comply with all applicable supervisory requirements (e.g., BACB rules, licensure requirements, funder and organization policies), including those related to supervision modalities and structure (e.g., in- person, video conference, individual, group)." Therefore, make fluency with the BACB supervision requirements a priority, and develop strategies for remaining up to date (e.g., calendar time to carefully review BACB newsletters when they arrive in your inbox and make to-do lists; regularly go to the website to review and download resources).

Specific to the meetings with your CS, *you* are responsible for maintaining the BACB required Consulting Supervision Documentation (BACB, May, 2021a). There are several things to be aware of regarding this documentation. You must use the BACB form to track all the meetings with your CS as the BACB will not accept any other forms for this documentation. The form has a spot at the top for you to enter your information (name, certification number, and date of certification) and then there are 12 sections to document each month. The BACB requires that the CS sign by the last of each month, but we recommend that you have the form prepared and ready to be signed in each meeting with your CS. In fact, that should be one of the last items on your standing agenda, just as you will do with your trainees. You need to store the form in a shared location and, at the conclusion of your first year, you and your CS both need to retain a copy of the completed BACB form. You both need to retain a copy for seven years and be ready to produce it should the BACB conduct an audit of the consulting supervision activities.

Consider each of the following and make yourself an actions list:

- Contract—Do you need to create or modify?
- Day/time/location of individual meetings.
- Day/time/location of group meetings, if applicable.
- Days/times of client observations.
- System of coordination with other supervisors, if applicable.
- Availability of a back-up supervisor if you cannot meet with trainee(s).
- File naming, storage, and sharing.
- BACB required documents.
- Documentation system for tracking hours, tasks, and feedback.
- Process for canceling and rescheduling meetings.
- Agenda—Who will manage and update?
    - Your CS will help you create an agenda template and plan for not only effectively managing your agenda, but also how to leverage the agenda as a critical-learning opportunity for your trainees.

Action	Materials Needed	Due Date	Completion Date

Preparing for CS Pre-Meeting

To maximize your time with your CS and your trainees, we recommend having a pre-meeting with your CS to get to know each other and to position you to start strong with your trainees. In this meeting, you'll have the opportunity to ask your CS some questions that will help you gain a fuller understanding of how they approach supervision and facilitate you developing your own approach to supervision. Some questions to consider asking are:

- What is your approach to supervision?
- What do you love most about supervising?
- What do you find most challenging about supervising?
- What is one thing you wish you learned sooner in your supervisory practice?
- What is something that new supervisors can do to maximize their time with their CS?

In the pre-meeting, your CS will model rapport-building activities, discuss some of their values related to supervision, and review the Values-Identification activity that you'll complete after the pre-meeting, review logistics (e.g., file storage, communication preferences), the contract, discuss how these workbooks will be used, and set up recurring meetings. Pay attention to how your CS carries out these activities, as you will be doing the same activities with your trainees.

Your CS will reach out to you to set up the pre-meeting and will develop an agenda. All you need to do is complete the Workload Assessment (on page 28) to discuss in the meeting. If you have completed your self-assessment and draft goals before the pre-meeting you can send them along; otherwise, just be sure to send them before the Month 1 meeting.

Workload Assessment Activity

Complete the Workload Assessment activity on the following page and be prepared to review it with your CS in the pre-meeting. You will complete and review the Workload Assessment with your CS every two months following the first month (i.e., in Months 3, 5, 7, 9, and 11). Conducting a thorough and ongoing assessment of your workload can highlight the current pulls on your time, allowing you to evaluate if you have the capacity to take on new tasks. Such an assessment, along with the results from evaluating the outcomes of your work tasks, can also facilitate a continual self-evaluation of your scope of competence. This information can also be used to help you assess and manage your stress and plan self-care activities. In the assessment, you will input the average weekly hours you spend on different activity types. In addition, you will list facilitators that support you in carrying out these activities (e.g., resources and systems provided to you or that you have already developed) and barriers that either make completing the tasks challenging or will require more time before the task can be completed (e.g., creating competencies and activities).

For the caseload sections you'll enter the average weekly number of hours you spend engaging in supervisory activities for each caseload category. Remember that the number of hours you spend supervising a client, RBT, BCaBA, or trainee is based on the number of hours of direct service received or worked, which will vary. That is why we recommend taking an average (e.g., calculate the weekly average from a 3-month period that is generally representative). The time you enter should include the time spent engaging in direct 1:1 and group-supervision contacts, as well as time spent on preparatory and follow-up tasks. In addition to time, fill in factors that facilitate completing the hours and tasks and those factors that present as barriers. For example, consider things like the variety and intensity of client and training needs; client/staff location (e.g., clinic-based, in-home, teleservice, combination); availability of effective systems and resources for providing and managing supervision and training; your level of experience and scope of competence; and availability of colleagues, supervisors, or mentors for clinical-case consult or problem-solving.

For the Professional Responsibilities column, think about all the other professional activities that you need to complete. These include regularly recurring tasks (e.g., scheduling, billing, reviewing data, attending standing meetings, writing progress reports, conducting staff performance assessments), as well as those that might not occur on a set schedule but still require your time (e.g., staff training, intake assessments, audits). For those tasks that do not occur regularly, consider reviewing the time spent on them over the last three to six months and adding that into your average.

There is no category in the assessment for listing out personal circumstances that impact work activities. Nonetheless, spend some time thinking about the pulls on your time from your life activities, especially any additional pulls that you can predict. For example, if you know that there is an upcoming medical procedure for you or someone for whom you are a caregiver, taking that into consideration will help you evaluate and plan for success. Some things to consider are overall level of stress and mental/physical health, time spent caring for others, and being enrolled in courses or other educational programs.

Task	Average Weekly Time Requirement	Facilitators	Barriers
Client Caseload Management			
RBT Caseload			
BCaBA Caseload			
Trainee Caseload			
Administrative Responsibilities			
Other Duties			
Total Average Weekly Work Hours:			

Getting Ready Summary

All right, you have put in a lot of time and effort to prepare for your upcoming efforts with your CS and your trainees. Well done! Take a breath and give yourself some well-deserved praise for taking a structured approach to starting your journey in supervision. The time you spend with your CS can be some of the most impactful experiences for you in your first year, as you develop your own supervisory style and practices and learn to navigate the critically important tasks of shaping others' repertoires. The time you spend with your trainees will be some of the most impactful experiences they have in shaping their clinical skills, as well as their supervisory skills. You can use the checklist to make sure that you did not miss any tasks from the Getting Ready section.

☑ Getting Ready Checklist

- ☐ Complete Reflection Activity (30-60 min.)

- ☐ Complete General Self-Assessment Questions (15 min).

- ☐ Complete the New Supervisor Self-Assessment Foundational Supervision Skills

    - ☐ Brief review (15 min.)

    - ☐ Review with mentor, past supervisor, or colleague (30 min.)

    - ☐ Complete the assessment (30 min.)

- ☐ Complete Goal Planning for New Supervisors Activity (30 min.)

- ☐ Complete My Resources Activity (15 min.)

- ☐ Complete Logistic Planning Activity (15 min.)

- ☐ Create your Planning for Supervision Actions List (15 min.)

- ☐ Complete the Workload Assessment and email to your CS before the Pre-Meeting

- ☐ Get and fill out the BACB Consulting Supervision Documentation document

- ☐ Email CS (before 1st or 2nd meeting)

    - ☐ Self-Assessment results

    - ☐ Draft-Goals

Next, you'll dive into the month-to-month section that covers the early months. Month 1 focuses on planning to manage the details of supervising trainees and building rapport with your CS. Optimally, you'll use the material in Month 1 before you start supervising trainees and as a basis for your first meeting with your CS. In your first CS meeting you will work to lay out the order of topics for the coming months, which might deviate from the order in which they appear, which is totally fine. This guidebook is meant to be flexible to meet your needs!

Getting Ready: Appendix A

Strategies for Finding a Consulting Supervisor

Use the strategies below if you are responsible for finding your own Consulting Supervisor (CS). These strategies are meant to assist you in identifying possible individuals who may be able to serve as your CS. Once you have some possible individuals identified, the strategies support you carrying out a structured and thoughtful approach to evaluating one or more individuals. Think of the process like a job search and interview. You want to do your best to ensure that you and your CS will be a good fit so that you maximize your time with them during your first year of supervision. Also, be prepared that you should sign a formal contract and pay for this service.

Step 1 – Evaluate Your Needs

Clearly assess and define your professional goals, desired outcomes, and exactly the types of supports you think you need (e.g., training and supervision, coaching, mentorship). You can use the activities in the Getting Ready section to help with this. Consider the context in which you'll be supervising, the types of clinical services, and the types of clients served. Identifying this information ahead of time will help ensure that you identify a CS with the right skills to support you. For example, supervising a group of trainees providing in-home only services over a wide geographic area using a mix of in-person and tele-supervision likely is much different than supervising a small group of trainees in a clinic-based setting. In the former case, you will benefit from a CS who has experience with that context, as it presents unique challenges and opportunities that are not present with exclusively in-clinic services. Characteristics of your context to consider include location of services, size of clinical team for each client, your client caseload, your supervisory caseload (i.e., number of behavior technicians, trainees, other personnel), type(s) of clinical services (e.g., standard early intervention, assessment and treatment of severe problem behavior or feeding needs, adult services, school-based services), available supports (e.g., you are a sole practitioner vs in a small agency with limited resources vs in a large agency with existing resources for supervising trainees).

- ☐ List your values.

- ☐ Do a self-assessment of your supervisory skills.

- ☐ Draft goals.

- ☐ Summarize your context.

Step 2 – Identify Possible Individuals

Once you have a good handle on your needs, start identifying individuals who might be appropriate to serve as your CS. Begin by listing anyone you might already know who may be able to serve as your CS or may know of others who would be great options to check out. For example, have a conversation with your current or former supervisor, professors, or leaders in your current or past job. If you are truly starting from scratch, you can do an internet search for those who might provide supervision to trainees, as they are in a good position to either provide CS services or recommend others. Because your CS must be certified by the BACB, you can also search the BACB's Certificant Registry to identify possible individuals. The Certificant Registry includes several search parameters (e.g., certificate level, geographic area, willingness to supervise) that you can use to help make your search more specific. In fact, even if you already have a list of possible individuals, it is a good idea to look them up in the Certificant Registry to verify that they are in good standing. If you are working in a state with licensure for behavior analysis, it is also worth checking with the applicable licensure board. Things to look for in the BACB Certificant Registry include the following:

- Are they willing to provide supervision?
- Do they meet the supervision requirements?
- Are they in your geographic area? (This might be irrelevant if video-conference meetings would be appropriate.)
- Are they "active" and in good standing (i.e., do they have any published disciplinary actions from the BACB)?

Step 3 – Contacting an Individual

Now it is time to reach out to one or more of the individuals on your list. If being able to meet in person is very important to you or your professional goals, prioritize contacting individuals within a drivable distance. For an individual you already know, this initial contact should be relatively easy. However, if you don't know the individuals, here are some ideas. If you have a colleague in common, consider asking your colleague to send an introductory email between you and the prospective CS. Alternatively, reach out directly to the individual via email to express your interest in having them serve as your CS. If you cannot find an email address, here are two ideas:

- If the individual is a certificant, you can contact them through their BACB Certificant Registry account. Use the "Find a Certificant" feature on the BACB's website to locate the certificant's Registry record and then click on their hyperlinked name next to "contact" to initiate a certificant contact through the Registry.

- Consider reaching out via social media to introduce yourself, describing why you are contacting them, and ask for their email address so that you can follow up.

If the individual replies that they cannot meet, consider asking if they might have one or more recommendations for others you can reach out to and if they might be willing to send an introductory email.

If an individual does not reply in a reasonable amount of time, try a follow-up communication. If you don't hear back, be compassionate and assume that competing contingencies are preventing them from getting back to you and move on to someone else. You may need to persist through several failed attempts; that's OKAY!

Sample Email

Below is a sample email to get you started:

> Dear Jane Doe,
>
> I hope this email finds you well. My name is Tyra Sellers, and I recently passed the BACB exam and am a new BCBA getting ready to supervise my first few trainees accruing their fieldwork experience hours. I am excited for this new adventure, but I am also really nervous. I take my supervisory duties very seriously. I am looking for someone to serve as my Consulting Supervisor for my first year, per the BACB requirements.
>
> I am sure that you are incredibly busy. Is there a possibility that you would be willing to discuss serving as my CS? You are likely familiar with the requirements, but just in case, this would require us to meet one-on-one once a month.
>
> If this is not something that you can fit into your busy schedule, I understand. If that is the case, would you consider putting me in touch with anyone you know who is providing CS services?
>
> Thank you for your kind consideration!
>
> Cheers,
>
> Tyra Sellers
> BCBA #1-03-1167

Step 4 – Prepare for the Meeting

Review the information you prepared from Step 1 so that you can clearly and succinctly describe what it is you are looking for. Prepare questions and discussion points for the meeting that will help you evaluate if this will be a good fit. Here are some questions to consider:

- What do you love about supervising? What do you find most challenging?

- What are your values related to providing supervision?

- How do you measure the success of your supervisees?

- How do you create opportunities for skill development?

- How do you go about creating a feedback-rich supervisory relationship?

- How do you evaluate the effects of your supervision?

- Have you ever supervised in the following contexts? Ask about contextual variables relevant to your needs and current context.

- Do you meet the BACB requirements to serve as a CS? How long have you been supervising?

- Do you have a contract that we can review?

- What are your fees?

Step 5 – Reflecting on the Meeting

After the meeting, evaluate the fit between the two of you. Consider how the conversation flowed and if it felt comfortable. Some things to reflect on are:

- Did it appear that your values seem to align?

- Did it appear that your communication styles are compatible?

- Could you detect that the relationship will be built on mutual respect and bi-directional feedback?

- Could you confirm that the individual has expertise in your area of interest or need?

- Did they appear prepared and organized?

- Did they answer your questions thoughtfully and thoroughly?

- Did they ask you questions?

If you determine that the person would be a good fit to serve as your CS, follow up with a call or email thanking them for their time and asking them if they would be willing to be your CS. In that email, include your expected start date and your availability for standing meetings. Consider letting them know that you are using this workbook and ask if they are familiar with the workbook pair. If not, ask if they would be willing to use the companion workbook for Consulting Supervisors so that you are both taking a similar, structured approach. If, on the other hand, you determine that the individual might not be a good fit, send them an email thanking them for their time and the opportunity to get to know them and let them know that you have identified another individual whose availability and skills best match your needs.

Getting Ready: Appendix B
Supervisor's Starter Resource List

Articles

Andzik, N. R., & Kranak, M. P. (2021). The softer side of supervision: Recommendations when teaching and evaluating behavior-analytic professionalism. *Behavior Analysis: Research and Practice, 21*(1), 65.

Barnes-Holmes, D. (2018). A commentary on the student-supervisor relationship: A shared journey of discovery. *Behavior Analysis in Practice, 11*, 174-176.

Becerra, L. A., Sellers, T. P. & Contreras, B. P. (2020). Maximizing the conference experience: Tips to effectively navigate academic conferences early in professional careers. *Behavior Analysis in Practice.* Advanced Online Publication. https://doi.org/10.1007/s40617-019-00406-w

Binder, C. (2016). Integrating organizational-cultural values with performance management. *Journal of Organizational Behavior Management, 36*(2-3), 185-201.

Brodhead, M. T. (2015). Maintaining professional relationships in an interdisciplinary setting: Strategies for navigating nonbehavioral treatment recommendations for individuals with autism. *Behavior Analysis in Practice, 8*, 70–78. doi: 10.1007/s40617-015-0042-7

Brodhead, M. T., Quigley, S. P., & Wilczynski, S. M. (2018). A call for discussion about scope of competence in behavior analysis. *Behavior Analysis in Practice, 11*(4), 424–435.

Carr, J. E., & Briggs, A. M. (2010). Strategies for making regular contact with the scholarly literature. *Behavior Analysis in Practice, 3*, 13-18.

Carr, J. E., Wilder, D. A., Majdalany, L., Mathisen, D., & Strain, L. A. (2013). An assessment based solution to a human-service employee performance problem. *Behavior Analysis in Practice, 6*, 16-32.

Cavalari, R. N., Gillis, J. M., Kruser, N., & Romanczyk, R. G. (2015). Digital communication and records in service provision and supervision: regulation and practice. *Behavior Analysis in Practice, 8*(2), 176-189.

Clark, H. B., Wood, R., Kuehnel, T., Flanagan, S., Mosk, M., & Northup, J. T. (1985). Preliminary validation and training of supervisory interactional skills. *Journal of Organizational Behavior Management, 7*, 95-115.

Conners, B., Johnson, A., Duarte, J., Murriky, R., & Marks, K. (2019). Future directions of training and fieldwork in diversity issues in applied behavior analysis. *Behavior Analysis in Practice, 12*, 1-10.

Critchfield, T. S., Doepke, K. J., Epting, L. K., Becirevic, A., Reed, D. D., Fienup, D., & Eccot, C. L. (2017). Normative emotional responses to behavior analysts or how not to use words to win friends and influence people. *Behavior Analysis in Practice, 10*, 97–106. https://doi.org/10.1007/s40617-016-0161-9.

Curry, S. M., Gravina, N. E., Sleiman, A. A., & Richard, E. (2019). The effects of engaging in rapport-building behaviors on productivity and discretionary effort. *Journal of Organizational Behavior Management, 39*(3-4), 213-226.

DiGennaro Reed, F. D., & Henley, A. J. (2015). A survey of staff training and performance management practices: The good, the bad, and the ugly. *Behavior Analysis in Practice*, 8(1), 16. https://doi.org/10.1007/s40617-015-0044-5.

Dounavi, K., Fennell, B., & Early, E. (2019). Supervision for certification in the field of applied behavior analysis: Characteristics and relationships with job satisfaction, burnout, work demands, and support. *International Journal of Environmental Research and Public Health, 16*(12), 2098. doi: 10.3390/ijerph16122098

Ehrlich, R.J., Nosik, M.R., Carr, J.E., & Wine, B. (2020). Teaching employees how to receive feedback: A preliminary investigation. *Journal of Organizational Behavior Management.* Advanced online publication. https://doi.org/10.1080/01608061.2020.1746470

Ellis, J. E., & Glenn, S. S. (1995). Behavior analytic repertoires: Where will they come from and how can they be maintained? *The Behavior Analyst, 18*(2), 285–292.

Fong, E. H., & Tanaka, S. (2013). Multicultural alliance of behavior analysis standards for cultural competence in behavior analysis. *International Journal of Behavioral Consultation and Therapy, 8*(2), 17.

Fong, E. H., Catagnus, R. M., Brodhead, M. T., Quigley, S., & Field, S. (2016). Developing the cultural awareness skills of behavior analysts. *Behavior Analysis in Practice, 9*, 84–94. doi:10.1007/s40617-016-0111-6

Fong, E. H., Ficklin, S., & Lee, H. Y. (2017). Increasing cultural understanding and diversity in applied behavior analysis. *Behavior Analysis: Research and Practice, 17*(2), 103–113. doi:10.1037/bar0000076

Garza, K. L., McGee, H. M., Schenk, Y. A., & Wiskirchen, R. R. (2018). Some tools for carrying out a proposed process for supervising experience hours for aspiring Board Certified Behavior Analysts®. *Behavior Analysis in Practice, 11*, 62-70.

Hajiaghamohseni, Z., Drasgow, E., & Wolfe, K. (2021). Supervision behaviors of board certified behavior analysts with trainees. *Behavior Analysis in Practice, 14*(1), 97-109.

Hantula, D. A. (2015). Job satisfaction: The management tool and leadership responsibility. *Journal of Organizational Behavior Management, 35*(1–2), 81–94.

Kruger, J., & Dunning, D. (1999). Unskilled and unaware of it: How difficulties in recognizing one's own incompetence lead to inflated self-assessments. *Journal of Personality and Social Psychology, 77*(6), 1121.

LaFrance, D. L., Weiss, M. J., Kazemi, E., Gerenser, J., & Dobres, J. (2019). Multidisciplinary teaming: Enhancing collaboration through increased understanding. *Behavior Analysis in Practice, 12*, 709-726.

Lau, R. S. & Cobb, A. T. (2010). Understanding the connections between relationship conflict and performance: The intervening roles of trust and exchange. *Journal of Organizational Behavior Management, 31*, 898–917. doi:10.1002/job.674

LeBlanc, L. A., Heinicke, M. R., & Baker, J. C. (2012). Expanding the consumer base for Behavior-analytic services: Meeting the needs of consumers in the 21st century. *Behavior Analysis in Practice, 5*, 4-14.

LeBlanc, L. A. & Luiselli, J. K. (2016). Refining supervisory practices in the field of behavior analysis: Introduction to the special section on supervision. *Behavior Analysis in Practice, 9*, 271-273.

LeBlanc, L. A., Sleeper, J. D., Mueller, J. R., Jenkins, S. R., & Harper-Briggs, A. M. (2020). Assessing barriers to effective caseload management by practicing behavior analysts. *Journal of Organizational Behavior Management, 39*(3-4), 317-336.

LeBlanc, L. A., Taylor, B. A., & Marchese N. V. (2019). The training experiences of behavior analysts: Compassionate care and therapeutic relationships with caregivers. *Behavior Analysis in Practice,* doi: 10.1007/s40617-019-00368-z

Leland, W., & Stockwell, A. (2019). A self-assessment tool for cultivating affirming practices with transgender and gender nonconforming (TGNC) clients, supervisees, students, and colleagues. *Behavior Analysis in Practice, 12,* 1-10.

Lindblad, T. L. (2021). Ethical Considerations in Clinical Supervision: Components of Effective Clinical Supervision Across an Interprofessional Team. *Behavior Analysis in Practice,* 1-13.

Maslach, C., & Jackson, S. E. (1981). The measurement of experienced burnout. *Journal of Organizational Behavior, 2,* 99–113.

Novak, M. D., Reed, F. D. D., Erath, T. G., Blackman, A. L., Ruby, S. A., & Pellegrino, A. J. (2019). Evidence-based performance management: Applying behavioral science to support practitioners. *Perspectives on behavior science, 42*(4), 955-972.

Parry-Cruwys, D., & MacDonald, J. Using Gamification to Promote Accurate Data Entry of Practicum Experience Hours in Graduate Students. *Behavior Analysis in Practice,* 1-10.

Pastrana, S., Frewing, T., Grow, L., Nosik, M., Turner, M., & Carr, J. (2016). Frequently assigned readings in behavior analysis graduate training programs. *Behavior Analysis in Practice, 3,* 1–7. https://doi.org/10.1007/s40617-016-0137-9

Plantiveau, C., Dounavi, K., & Virués-Ortega, J. (2018). High levels of burnout among early career board-certified behavior analysts with low collegial support in the work environment. *European Journal of Behavior Analysis, 19*(2), 195-207. doi: 10.1080/15021149.2018.1438339

Sellers, T. P., Alai-Rosales, S., & MacDonald, R. P. (2016). Taking full responsibility: The ethics of supervision in behavior-analytic practice. *Behavior Analysis in Practice, 9,* 299-308.

Sellers, T. P., LeBlanc, L. A. & Valentino, A. V. (2016). Recommendations for detecting and addressing barriers to successful supervision. *Behavior Analysis in Practice, 9,* 309-319. doi: 10.1007/s40617-016-0142-z

Sellers, T. P., Valentino, A. L., Landon, T.J., & Aiello, S. (2019). Board certified behavior analysts' supervisory practices of trainees: Survey results and recommendations. *Behavior analysis in practice, 12*(3), 536-546.

Sellers, T. P., Valentino, A. L., & LeBlanc, L. A. (2016). Recommended practices for individual supervision of aspiring behavior analysts. *Behavior Analysis in Practice, 9,* 274-286. doi:10.1007/s40617-016-0110-7

Taylor, B. A., LeBlanc, L. A., & Nosik, M. R. (2019). Compassionate care in behavior analytic treatment: Can outcomes be enhanced by attending to relationships with caregivers? *Behavior Analysis in Practice, 12,* 654-666.

Turner, L. B., Fischer, A. J., & Luiselli, J. K. (2016). Towards a competency-based, ethical, and socially valid approach to the supervision of applied behavior analytics. *Behavior Analysis in Practice, 9*, 287-298. doi: 10.1007/s40617-016-0121-4

Valentino, A. L., LeBlanc, L. A., & Sellers, T. P. (2016). The benefits of group supervision and a recommended structure for implementation. *Behavior Analysis in Practice, 9*(4), 320-328.

Walker, S., & Sellers, T. (2021). Teaching appropriate feedback reception skills using computer-based instruction: A systematic replication. *Journal of Organizational Behavior Management,* 1-19.

Wright, P. I. (2019). Cultural humility in the practice of applied behavior analysis. *Behavior Analysis in Practice, 12*, 805-809.

BACB Documents and Resources

Note: The BACB makes regular updates and changes to requirements, resources, and documents. Be sure to check the website for the most current information and resources.

- *BACB Eligibility Requirements* (BCBA, September 2021)
- *BACB Sample Supervision Contract for BCBA/BCaBA Trainees* (BACB, n.d.b.)
- *BCBA® Board Certified Behavior Analysts Handbook* (BCBA, May 2021)
- *Consulting Supervisor Requirements for New BCBAs Supervising Fieldwork* (BCBA, May 2021)
- *Ethics Code for Behavior Analysts* (BACB, 2020)
- *Final Experience Verification Form: Individual Supervisor* (BACB, August 2021a)
- *Monthly Fieldwork Verification Form Individual Supervisor 2022 Fieldwork requirements* (BACB, August 2021b)
- *Supervision Training Curriculum Outline (2.0)* (BACB 2018)

Books

Bailey, J. & Burch, M. (2010). *25 Essential Skills & Strategies for the Professional Behavior Analyst.* New York, NY: Routledge.

Britton, L. N., & Cicoria, M. J. (2019). *Remote Fieldwork Supervision for BCBA® Trainees.* Academic Press.

Carnegie, D. (1936). *How to Win Friends and Influence People.* Simon and Schuster.

Courtney, W. T., Hartley, B. K., LaMarca, V. J., Rosswurm, M., & Reid, D. H. (2017). *Trainee Manual: The Training Curriculum for Supervisors of ABA Technicians in Autism Programs.* Sloan Publishing.

Daniels, A. C., & Bailey, J. S. (2014). *Performance Management: Changing Behavior that Drives Organizational Effectiveness.* Atlanta, GA: Aubrey Daniels International. *Multi-Tiered Systems of Support,* 27.

Kazemi, E., Rice, B., & Adzhyan, P. (2018). *Fieldwork and Supervision for Behavior Analysts: A Handbook.* Springer Publishing Company.

LeBlanc, L. A., Sellers, T. P., Shahla Ala'i. (2020). *Building and Sustaining Meaningful and Effective Relationships as a Supervisor and Mentor.* Sloan Publishing.

Patterson, K., Grenny, J., McMillan, R., & Switzler A. (2012). *Crucial Conversations: Tools for Talking When Stakes are High.* McGraw Hill.

Reid, D. H., Parsons, M. B., & Green, C. W. (2012). *The Supervisor's Guidebook: Evidence-based Strategies for Promoting Work Quality and Enjoyment Among Human Service Staff.* Morganton, NC: Habilitative Management Consultants.

Wentz, F. H. (2013). *10 Things Employers Expect Their Employees to Know: A Soft Skills Workbook.* Author.

Podcasts

Where possible we have indicated specific episode numbers. However, because not all podcasts use episode numbers, we encourage you to visit the podcast websites and conduct your own search for relevant episodes.

ABA Inside Track
Supervision Related Episodes
https://www.abainsidetrack.com/previous-episodes

Behavior Babe Podcast
https://www.behaviorbabe.com/podcast-episodes

Central Reach The Behavioral View
Episode 11
https://centralreach.com/resources/the-behavioral-view/

Functional Relations Podcast
Episodes: Season 3, Episode 1 & 3
https://www.functionalrelationspodcast.com/

Operant Innovations Podcast
Episodes 015 & 016
https://abatechnologies.com/operant-innovations-podcast

Shades of Behavior
Episodes June 20th, 2020
https://anchor.fm/shadesofaba

The Behavioral Observations Podcast
Episodes 29, 13, 46, 88, 90, 95, 147, 148, 199
https://behavioralobservations.com/

The Lift
https://abatechnologies.com/operant-innovations-podcast/for-ce-credit

Why We Do What We Do
Episode 054
https://wwdwwdpodcast.com/

Month-to-Month Guides
The Early Months

This next section provides you with structure for the first three months of activities with your CS and your trainees. There are two sections in each month. The first section outlines tasks related to your CS meeting and covers what to do before, during, and after the meeting. The second section focuses on tasks for your trainee meeting and organizes the tasks in the same order of before, during, and after the meeting. These first three months are pre-set because the topics of those months are important for anyone who is beginning to supervise. They focus on building strong relationships, managing logistics and stress, assessing your own needs and those of your trainee, and planning your curriculum based on those needs.

Note that you only have one required meeting per month with your CS; however, you will have more than one meeting with your trainee. You will need to follow the BACB requirements regarding the number of contacts and direct observations with clients per month. In addition, you are likely to periodically have other meetings as opportunities present themselves or needs arise. Some activities that can only be observed when they naturally occur include your trainee conducting a staff or caregiver training, a staff performance review, or a client-intake assessment. Therefore, it is your responsibility to divide the activities described for trainees in the monthly section across appropriate subsequent meetings or contacts in that month. Your CS can help you identify which activities are best carried out in your trainee meeting in a given month. To demonstrate what this might look like, we have divided the Month 1 trainee activities across meetings A and B. Remember that the content for Month 4 through Month 11 will be designed by you and your CS using the information from assessments, from the skills-specific section, and other resources.

Each month contains preparation activities, meeting activities, and follow-up activities. Each of those activities focuses on tasks to enhance your skills as a supervisor, as well as tasks to help you prepare for the upcoming month of activities with your trainees. Activities may require you to reflect, plan, carry out actions, and/or evaluate and discuss the results of your actions. There is a mixture of tasks, some of which you will complete on your own, with your trainees, and in collaboration with your CS. We also provide ideas for activities and tasks that are best carried out within the CoP you have (or are) creating. Even if your CoP begins as just you and a colleague it is worthwhile to establish it now and cultivate and grow it over time.

This workbook and your activities are designed to create a first year of supervising that is dynamic and multifaceted. Picture an infinity symbol with you, as the new CS in the center. The loop on the left represents your CS and the loop on the right, your trainees (or other supervisees). Your CS is engaging in self-reflection, assessment, and planning activities to grow their skill set and assist you in doing the same. At the same time, you are engaging in self-reflection, assessment, and planning activities to grow your repertoires. You are then guiding and assisting your trainees in doing similar self-reflections, self-assessments, and goal planning. Finally, all your efforts flow back around to you as you evaluate your practices and their effects and then review things with your CS for continual improvement.

Creating this infinite flow of information is a tall order, but one that we think you will find enjoyable and transformative. In your efforts with your trainee, you will need to impact their knowledge and skills of behavior analysis as well as their pivotal professional repertoires (e.g., interpersonal communication, organization and time management, problem-solving) so that they become well prepared to succeed as a future clinician and supervisor. At this point you are well positioned to start your varied supervisory relationships off on the right foot! You have engaged in thoughtful reflection, assessment, and planning. So, for now, take a deep breath and let's get started with Month 1!

Month 1
Planning Logistics and Building Relationships

Goals for upcoming CS meeting	**Goals for upcoming trainee meetings**
• Review Pre-meeting.	• Build rapport.
• Review Workload Assessment.	• Establish importance of supervision and feedback.
• Plan specific tasks to address logistics with your trainees.	• Complete logistics.
• Plan specific tasks for building collaborative relationship with trainees.	• Ensure access to important documents.
	• Complete and review Collaboration Activity for Trainees.

 Month 1 CS Meeting Activities

Before Month 1 Meeting with Your CS

Complete the following tasks in preparation of your upcoming Month 1 meeting with your CS.

PREP TASK 1 – Review: Go back and look over the tasks from the Getting Ready section, reflect on how things went in the pre-meeting, organize documents (contracts, BACB documents), and make sure that you sent your self-assessment and draft goals to your CS.

PREP TASK 2 – Prepare for Logistics: In your pre-meeting with your CS, they carried out several logistics-related activities with you (e.g., reviewing and signing the contract, deciding on document sharing and communication methods). You will be doing the same activities with your trainees in your first meeting with them. To set yourself up for success, reflect on how your CS carried out those activities and draft questions you want to review with your CS related to trainee logistics. Make sure that you have all the documents for your trainees ready to go, especially if you would like to review them with your CS. Here are some topics to consider reviewing with your CS:

- The initial agenda for your trainee supervision meetings (we have provided you a template for your first meeting that you can use or modify).
- The agenda you'll create to plan your observations (we have provided you a sample that you can use or modify).
- Trainee contract to ensure it meets all requirements.
- Tracking documents for hours, topics, and feedback.
- Recommendations for managing shared documents and carrying out reviews/edits.
- Structure for effectively using group supervision if this is an option for your trainees.

PREP TASK 3 – Values-Identification Activity: You and your CS discussed the importance of identifying your professional values related to practice and supervising others. They shared their values with you, and you likely shared some of your initial thoughts about your values. Your CS reviewed this activity with you at the end of your pre-meeting. Now, take some time to reflect on that conversation and complete the table below. Describe your values for yourself as a supervisor and the strategies that you want to use during supervision with your trainees. You can refer to LeBlanc, Sellers et al. (2020) Chapter 3 for additional support and guidance in these self-reflection activities. You will review this activity with your CS in the upcoming Month 1 meeting and discuss how this information can be used to help you build rapport with your trainees.

Domain	Value	Example of Behaving Consistently with this Value	Strategy for Conveying this Value to Your Trainee
Practice			
Supervision			

PREP TASK 4 – Prepare Feedback Activity: One of the keys to a successful supervisory relationship is establishing effective bi-directional feedback from day one. This means that you need to be prepared to talk about this in the very first meeting with your trainee. Think about your history with receiving and giving feedback and take stock of your related skills. Think about how you will ask your trainee to share their experiences with feedback and learn about their preferences. Think about how you will describe what bi-directional feedback is, why it is critically important, and how you and your trainee will engage in it. Review the sample scripts provided. Now draft out some scripts for how you will talk about these things with your trainees in your first meeting. For more examples of scripts, see the LeBlanc, Sellers et al. (2020) supervision and mentorship book. Don't worry if this feels weird, or you aren't sure what to write. You'll review the scripts with your CS and practice if needed. Also, begin to think about how you will collect formal feedback. For example, will you use an anonymous form or a document you can give your trainees to provide structured feedback? We provide a sample feedback form and prompts across the months to solicit formal feedback from your trainees. Draft your scripts on the following page.

Sample Feedback Starter Scripts

- I'd love to hear about your past experiences with receiving feedback. What types of "feedback givers" have you experienced in the past?

- When I say "bi-directional feedback" I mean that feedback flows both ways between us and that it impacts both of us.

- Feedback is really important because it is one of the most direct and immediate ways that we can impact each other's behavior.

- I am committed to your success, which means I will be providing a lot of feedback to you. I am going to do my best to create a trusting relationship so that you can also help me improve by telling me what is working well and what might need some tweaking.

Questions to learn about trainee's history with feedback: _____

_____

_____

_____

Describing bi-directional feedback: _____

_____

_____

_____

Describing why feedback is critical: _____

_____

_____

_____

Describing how you and trainee will implement bi-directional feedback: _____

_____

_____

_____

PREP TASK 5 – Prepare Collaboration Activity for Trainees: Your CS engaged in rapport building with you during the pre-meeting, which is something that you'll do with your trainees. One way to build rapport and start strong is to engage in collaboration activities. Review the Collaboration Activity for Trainees in Appendix A that you will ask your trainees to complete during your first month of supervisory activities and prepare any questions you have for your CS related to how you should introduce or review the Collaboration Activity for Trainees with your trainees. Remember, you are *not* completing this activity; rather you are reviewing it so that if you have any questions about how to introduce and carry out this activity with your trainee, you can ask your CS in the upcoming meeting. The Collaboration Activity for Trainees can be found in Appendix A for your review and to copy and present to your trainee.

The purpose of this activity is to set the stage for a strong, collaborative relationship between supervisor and trainee. This activity focuses on giving your trainee a structured opportunity to think about and discuss topics like receiving and giving feedback and goals that they may have for themselves. Having your trainees complete this activity and then reviewing it with them increases the likelihood that your trainee will feel comfortable having a discussion about these topics, as they will come into the conversation having had the opportunity to reflect on and develop their answers. This can be helpful for individuals who may feel put on the spot when asked these types of questions and struggle coming up with a meaningful response in the moment. During your first month of supervision, you will give this activity to your trainee in your first meeting and review it in your second meeting. In preparing for this activity, think about how you will present this activity to your trainee. We recommend briefly describing the activity and the purpose of it and pausing to ask open-ended questions to ensure your trainee understands the goal of the activity. Next, we suggest you take the time to review each item, give a brief rationale, and invite questions. Finally, give your trainee a clear due date and tell them how they should get the completed activity to you (e.g., email, save in shared folder). Be prepared to discuss your plan for presenting this activity when you meet with your CS.

Checklist for Preparing for CS Month 1 Meeting

- ☐ Review information and tasks completed from Getting Ready section (make sure you have the Consulting Supervision Documentation form ready).

- ☐ Outline trainee logistics, related questions, and have trainee contract and other documents (e.g., 1st meeting agenda, template for observing, spreadsheet for tracking hours and feedback) ready for review.

- ☐ Complete Workload Assessment (assigned at end of pre-meeting with CS).

- ☐ Complete Values Identification Activity.

- ☐ Complete Feedback Activity.

- ☐ Review Collaboration Activity for Trainee and prepare questions.

These are the activities that will occur during your Month 1 meeting with your CS. The purpose of these activities is to prepare you to have a successful first month of supervision with your trainees. Your CS will provide the agenda for this meeting. In addition to completing these activities, pay attention to the tone your CS sets for the conversations, how they run the meeting, and how they use the agenda.

1. **Review your Workload Assessment**: Your CS will facilitate a review of your workload assessment. Focus on discussing any barriers that you identified, particularly related to your trainee caseload. This is also a great time to begin a conversation about topics such as organization, time management, stress management, and self-care. You can also ask your CS to share how they approach assessing their workload and how they use that information to support managing their time and making decisions about taking on new tasks.

2. **Discuss Agendas**: your CS will review the importance of agendas, the critical features of an agenda, how agendas will be used in your meetings with them, how you should use agendas to facilitate your organization and time management of your supervisory practices, and how your agenda can be leveraged to teach those skills to your trainees.

   Notes: _____

   _____

   _____

3. **Review Trainee Logistics and Contract**: You will present your plan for addressing trainee logistics (e.g., scheduling meetings, document sharing) and reviewing the contract and asking your CS questions. Your CS might ask you to role-play how you are going to introduce, discuss, and answer questions about the trainee contract. During this time, you will show your CS your agenda for your first meeting(s) with your trainees and a template for conducting observations. Your CS will review the basics of an effective agenda so that you are well prepared to develop your own agenda for subsequent trainee meetings in the first and second months of supervision. Use the Notes section to jot down ideas and scripts to help you cover logistics, review the contract with your trainees, and tasks related to making the agenda for your Month 2 CS meeting.

   Notes: _____

   _____

   _____

4. **Review Values Identification Activity**: Review the results of this activity and discuss with your CS how you can use this information to support your initial rapport-building activities in your first month of supervision with your trainees. If you are nervous about how to discuss your experiences and values related to supervision with your trainees, you can role-play with your CS during this time. Use the Notes section to jot down ideas and scripts to help you engage in rapport building with your trainees.

   Notes: _____

   _____

   _____

5. **Review Feedback Starter Questions and Scripts**: Your CS is going to facilitate a discussion about feedback, focusing on things like what bi-directional feedback is, why it is critical for a successful supervisory relationship, and why it is important to learn about your trainees' histories and preferences related to feedback. Review your starters for asking questions and discussing feedback and make revisions. If you are nervous about doing this activity with your trainees, take this time to practice with your CS. Use the Notes section to jot down ideas and scripts to help you facilitate an open conversation with trainees about feedback.

   Notes: _____

   _____

   _____

6. **Review Plan for Collaboration Activity for Trainees**: Discuss your plan to review this activity with your trainees at the end of your first supervision meeting. This is the time to ask your CS questions about how to frame your presentation of the activity and your expectation that your trainees complete the activity on their own and review it in a subsequent meeting during the first month of supervision. Also discuss how you plan to review the activity and develop some scripts for you to use to praise efforts and address subjects such as how to support trainees in providing you with feedback. Use the Notes section to jot down ideas and scripts to help you facilitate an open conversation with trainees about the Collaboration Activity for Trainees.

   Notes: _____

   _____

   _____

7. **Wrap-Up**: Review assigned tasks and/or readings and due dates. Confirm date and time of next meeting. Ask your CS to sign the Consulting Supervision Document form.

Review the items covered and plan time in your calendar to make any needed adjustments to your items for your first month of supervision with your trainees and to complete tasks for your Month 2 CS meeting.

Month 1 Trainee Meeting and Observation Activities

Complete the following tasks in preparation of your upcoming first month of supervision activities with your trainees. Remember that you will have more than one contact with your trainees throughout the month and at least one of those contacts will be a direct observation with a client. How you meet BACB requirements depends on your setting and other factors, such as use of group supervision and if you are the only supervisor. For this first month of supervisory activities, we have broken the activities into two meetings to demonstrate how the information and tasks might be distributed and reviewed across two meetings in a month and we have also provided guidance for planning your observation time with the trainee or supervisee. For subsequent months, we describe the general activities for the span of the supervisory meetings and observations that will occur in the month; it is up to you to distribute them across the meetings you schedule with your trainees. It is also important to remember the focus of this workbook is on how to engage in high-quality supervisory practices, not what behavior-analytic content or items from the BACB Task List you should cover when with your trainees. Therefore, it is also your responsibility to add clinical and client-specific tasks to your trainees' meeting agendas, as we cannot predict when you may be covering specific clinical content.

Before Month 1 Meeting A with Your Trainee

As you plan for your first supervision meeting with your trainee, remember the primary goals: build rapport, establish importance of supervision and feedback, complete logistics (e.g., contract, scheduling). It might be helpful to keep in mind the 5 critical characteristics that can impact the perceived quality of a meeting:

1. use of an agenda,
2. notetaking,
3. punctuality,
4. having an appropriate environment, and
5. having a meeting leader (Leach et al., 2009).

For more resources preparing for your first meetings with your trainee, review the information presented in Sellers, Valentino, et al. (2016).

PREP TASK 1 – Prepare Meeting and Observation Agendas: Create the agendas for the meetings and observations you'll complete in your first month. We have provided samples for you.

Sample Agenda for 1st Trainee Meeting

1. Welcome to the Experience! Let's get to know each other (10–15 min.)

    a. Discuss importance of supervision and BACB requirements

    b. My background and experience as a supervisor, my life, interests, and guiding values

    c. Your background and experiences, your life, interests, and guiding values

2. Logistics

    a. Contract Review and Questions (20 min.)

    b. Discuss and decide on: communication methods, file sharing and storage, expectation for managing BACB required experience documents (10 min.)

3. Brief feedback conversation (10 min.)

4. Wrap-Up (5 min.)

    a. Introduce Trainee Collaboration Activity

    b. Review any other tasks (e.g., getting documents, setting up an account for the agreed upon file sharing platform)

    c. Planning for next contact

        i. Set the appointment

        ii. Create an actions list for follow-up tasks

Sample Direct Observation Supervision Agenda

Trainee: _____ Date of Observation/Supervision Session: _____

Client Initials (if applicable): _____ Context of Observation: _____

1. Greet the supervisee and discuss goals for observation (e.g., observe specific programs, conduct functional assessment probes, collect IOA data, train on a new program, answer any questions) (3-5 min.)

2. Review prior progress notes, examine graphs, identify any required changes to the programs (10 min.)

3. Observe program 1 (insert name of program here) (5-10 min.)

    a. Observe for at least 5 minutes or a minimum of 5 trials

    b. Collect procedural integrity data and calculate accuracy

    c. Collect IOA data for their primary data and calculate agreement

4. Provide feedback on performance for program 1 using best practices for feedback delivery (5-10 min.)

    a. Provide feedback on accuracy of implementation, quality of data, any things done well, any things that need to change and consider modeling if appropriate

5. Provide training on a new program (20-30 min.)

    a. Briefly explain the program, why it matters, and give the supervisee the written protocol, the procedural integrity data sheet, and a one-page cheat sheet (i.e., the instructions step of BST)

    b. Model implementation of the program while they score your implementation using the data sheet

    c. Debrief about that implementation (e.g., how did I do, I did this because, etc.)

    d. Ask if they have any questions about the program or whether they would like to see it implemented again before trying it themselves

    e. Either demonstrate again or have them begin rehearsal and feedback until they meet criterion

6. Wrap-Up and feedback (5 min.)

    a. Provide an overall summary of session, with high points, and areas to focus on

    b. Ask if they have any feedback on supervision or any questions

    c. Indicate when the next observation will be

    d. Create a next actions list if appropriate

    e. Sign any relevant forms and documentation

Create an observation agenda and form if your organization does not have a standard one. It should have general areas of observation as well as specific data-based evaluation areas.

Sample Observation Form

General Areas to Observe: Use a checkmark if observed and acceptable, a slash if observed and there is a concern, and n/a if there was no opportunity to observe.

☐ appearance   ☐ materials ready   ☐ demeanor during session

☐ on-time   ☐ began session with   ☐ completed session note
                        rapport building
☐ organized

Session Specific Data:

☐ Implemented programs with integrity (use program-specific procedural integrity forms)
  Score:
  Notes: _____

☐ Implemented behavior plan with integrity (use plan-specific, procedural integrity form)
  Score:
  Notes: _____

☐ Interobserver agreement
  Score:
  Notes: _____

☐ Positive, fun, engaging interactions with the client throughout the session

  Notes: _____

Session Observation Summary:
Summary of Successes:

Summary of Opportunity for Improvement:

Assigned Tasks (if applicable):
  1.
  2.
  3.
  4.

Documentation of Review: Initial below documents that the results of the observation were reviewed with the trainee. Note that the date of the observation and review should be within 3 days of each other. If the review occurs more than three days after the observation date, provide a brief explanation.

Review Date: _____   Trainee Initials: _____   Supervisor Initials: _____

PREP TASK 2 – Gather Documents: Prepare by making sure you have all the needed documents for your first month of meetings. This includes things like the contract, agendas, observation form, trainee tracking system to document each contact (we provided some considerations and a sample in Appendix B) and any BACB documents you'll need.

PREP TASK 3 – Draft Logistics: You'll make many of the logistics decisions collaboratively with your trainee, but you should come prepared with some options and some hard requirements. For example, it is recommended that you make it a clear requirement that all BACB-required documents be completed in a meeting with you at the appropriate time each month. List out options for meeting days/times, observation windows, preferred methods of communication, file storage/sharing platforms. Think about how you will present this topic and facilitate your trainee expressing their preferences.

PREP TASK 4 – Prepare and Practice Feedback Scripts: Spend some time reviewing the notes you made during your CS meeting and prepare scripts or starters for your discussion about feedback with your trainees. Prioritize doing this with as much time as possible before your first trainee meeting in case you need to send the draft scripts to your CS for feedback.

PREP TASK 5 – Prepare the Collaboration Activity for Trainees: Review your notes from the meeting with your CS and the Collaboration Activity for Trainees (Appendix A). Reflect on how you will present this activity to your trainee and how you will discuss the importance of building a collaborative relationship that includes bi-directional feedback.

PREP TASK 6 – Schedule Reflection Time: Schedule time in your calendar within a day or two after your first trainee meeting to reflect and start making notes in the Month 1 Reflection activity table (in the "After Meeting B" section). Schedule more time following your last trainee meeting or observation in Month 1 to add more notes. You will complete the activity in preparation for your Month 2 CS meeting.

Checklist for Preparing for Trainee Month 1 Meeting A

- ☐ Make agendas and observation forms.

- ☐ Create and gather documents.

- ☐ Draft logistics options.

- ☐ Prepare feedback scripts.

- ☐ Prepare Collaboration Activity for Trainees.

- ☐ Schedule time to reflect and makes notes on trainee meetings and observations in the Month 1 Reflection activity table.

1. **Introductions and Rapport Building:** You'll begin the meeting by briefly reviewing the agenda and engaging in rapport building activities. Spend some time getting to know each other. You can provide a summary of your professional experiences, focusing on your path into ABA and what you love about supervision. This is where you can share a bit about your values related to supervision. Be careful to balance the time you spend talking about yourself with the time you spend asking questions about your trainee and summarizing the information they share. Make a concerted effort to spend more time listening than talking. Once you both appear comfortable, transition into the remainder of the meeting by returning to the agenda and remaining tasks for the meeting. For example, you can say something like, "I am really enjoying getting to know you and I am excited about your interest in ABA! We have a lot to cover for the remainder of the meeting, so let's review the agenda."

   ### Agenda Pro Tip

   On your copy of the agenda track the actual time spent on each activity. After the meeting review the agenda, making notes of the differences between your estimates and actual times (and if you had to rush or end an activity after going overtime). Review your data with your CS.

2. **Logistics:** Move into the logistics portion of the conversation by introducing the contract and taking time to review it section by section and inviting questions along the way. Once the contract is reviewed and signed, move to talking about the other logistics you have listed, such as identifying standing meetings day/times, reviewing the BACB requirements and signature documents, exchanging contact information, preferred ways for letting each other know if one if running late or needs to cancel, and where documents will be stored. Do your best to be collaborative during this portion of the meeting, rather than directive. Where possible, share burdens or inconveniences. For example, instead of leading by listing out your preferences for document storage, you could ask the trainee which platforms or systems they are most comfortable with and currently have access to. In other words, be willing to accept an inconvenience such as learning a new storage system or moving one of your standing meetings to make room for their most optimal meeting day/time instead of expecting your trainee to bear the burden of most of the inconveniences. Introduce the importance of agendas, their primary functions, and how you will use them (e.g., where they will be stored, when they will be ready before the next meeting, who is initially responsible for what regarding agendas). When discussing tracking systems, if your trainee does not have one for the ongoing tracking of their fieldwork experience and supervision hours and activities, briefly describe the needed components and assign creating one as a task for the next meeting.

3. **Feedback Discussion:** Next, you'll complete a brief discussion about feedback. This is meant to just introduce the topic of feedback, its importance, and the concept of bi-directional feedback. The idea is to get them used to hearing about and talking about feedback. You will cover this in more depth in your second meeting with them in your first month of supervisory activities. You can let them know that you are going to focus on creating a feedback-rich environment and that you know that might be different from their experiences in the past with other supervisors, managers, or leaders. Let them know that it is okay to be a little nervous about this, and that you are going to complete specific activities to help you both establish a good feedback loop. You should also let them know that you'll be providing opportunities for formal feedback, using a structured form, throughout the supervisory relationship.

4. **Assign Collaboration Activity for Trainees:** The last portion of the meeting involves introducing the Collaboration Activity for Trainees (Appendix A). You reviewed this activity and discussed it with your CS, so you should be well prepared to review it with your trainee. Have the activity saved in a separate document that you can show on your screen or print it out for review. Introduce the activity, review it, describe the purpose for the activity, and be sure to solicit and answer any questions. Finally, clearly indicate when the activity must be completed (e.g., 48 hours before your next meeting to allow you time to review it and get prepared to discuss it in your next meeting). There is a spot for the due date at the top of the activity, consider pre-filling it out for your trainee. In addition to indicating the due date, be clear about how you want them to share it with you. Do you want it emailed to you or saved to the file-sharing platform you have agreed to use?

5. **Wrap-Up:** End the meeting by thanking your trainee for the time and participation. Express your appreciation for the information they shared and for this opportunity to collaboratively learn and grow. Review the next steps, any assigned tasks or readings, and due dates. For example, let them know that you will email them or post the signed contract to the shared-storage system. Review any tasks for them to complete (e.g., thinking about their goals for supervision, reading any BACB required materials or reviewing the BACB website, obtaining any required documents from their employer). End the meeting by confirming your next scheduled meeting date and time and telling them to reach out with any questions that might come up after the meeting. If needed, prompt them to have you sign any needed forms.

After Month 1 Meeting A with Your Trainee

After the first meeting with your trainee, you'll need to complete any tasks that you identified in the meeting. For example:

- Set up recurring meetings and observations in your calendar and consider inviting trainee.
- Document assigned tasks and due dates so that you can collect data on timeliness (e.g., in spreadsheet, in your calendar).
- Set up any needed folders in the identified shared-storage system.
- Add any needed documents (e.g., BACB forms or documents) to the shared-storage system.
- Send or share meeting notes.
- Send or save a signed contract.
- Send or save the Collaboration Activity for Trainees.

It's also nice to send a brief note via email or text message, thanking your trainee for their time, restating your enthusiasm for your supervisory relationship, and confirming the next meeting date and time. Not only does this express your commitment to the success of the relationship, but it also models appropriate professional behavior for your trainee.

Before Month 1 Meeting B with Your Trainee

As you plan for your second supervision meeting with your trainee you still have the same primary goals: build rapport, establish importance of supervision and feedback, complete logistics (e.g., contract, scheduling).

PREP TASK 1 – Prepare Meeting and Observation Agendas: Prepare the agenda. If needed, revise the format you used for your first trainee meeting agendas. You should focus on identifying recurring items and an appropriate flow of the topics and tasks. Remember to include estimates for how long you intend to spend on each item. Things to consider including in your second Month 1 meeting are:

1. Review last meeting and any tasks (e.g., creating accounts or accessing the document-sharing system).
2. Review observations that occurred since the last meeting.
3. Review Collaboration Activity for Trainees and Feedback Discussion.
4. Review client-related items.
5. Review behavior-analytic content, items for the BACB Task List, items from the Ethics Code for Behavior Analysts.
6. Review BACB website and discuss BACB Scavenger Hunt activity (Appendix C; as the BACB website is updated frequently, you made need to update the scavenger hunt items).
7. Wrap-up: review new tasks/reading, due dates, and next meeting.

PREP TASK 2 – Review Meeting and Observation Notes: Prepare for reviewing how things have been going and discuss the observations you have conducted. Depending on how the observations went, you may need to build in time for some explicit training. Reflect on how your interactions with your trainees have gone and if there is anything you need to do differently.

PREP TASK 3 – Preview the Completed Collaboration Activity for Trainees: Check to see if the trainee completed the Collaboration Activity by the due date. If not, provide immediate feedback in person (preferred), via a phone call, or in an email with a reminder to get it completed. If they did, review their responses and prepare how you will review the activity with them.

PREP TASK 4 – Review and Prepare for the BACB Scavenger Hunt Activity: The purpose of this activity is to make sure that your trainee is aware of and familiar with the BACB. Specifically, they need to know the role of the BACB, the requirements that apply to trainees, and the resources available to support them during their fieldwork experience. Moreover, this is a time for you to discuss not only the BACB, but other important entities, as relevant (e.g., licensure boards, professional associations). Therefore, it is critical that you are fluent with the BACB requirements and where information and resources are located on the BACB website. If you are not as fluent as you would like to be, consider calendaring several short times (e.g., 15-30 min) each day to review the information.

Checklist for Preparing for Trainee Month 1 Meeting B

☐ Make agendas and observation forms.

☐ Review notes.

☐ Prepare scripts or starters for conversations.

☐ Preview the completed Collaboration Activity for Trainees.

☐ Prepare for the BACB Scavenger Hunt Activity.

1. **Check In:** Start your meeting by checking in with your trainee. Ask them how things are going. If you have any specific information from the last meeting (e.g., they had a test coming up, they were planning on seeing a movie or going to a concert) ask specific follow-up questions. Then introduce the agenda and briefly review it. Remember that agenda pro tip from meeting A? Well, don't forget to track your actual time for each item; review and make notes.

2. **Review Last Meeting:** Briefly review the last meeting and discuss how it went. Review any tasks that were due following that meeting and address any issues with logistics. For example, ensure that they can access the file-sharing system and that shared calendar events are showing up for them.

3. **Review Observations and Products:** Review notes you have from the client observations you conducted of the trainee working with clients and any products (e.g., session notes) you reviewed. Provide feedback and any training related to the observation (e.g., modeling how to run a program or complete a session note). If applicable, assign any resulting tasks (e.g., review client's program, observe staff X conducting specific program) and ensure your trainee understands the expectations.

4. **Review the Collaboration Activity for Trainees and Discuss Feedback:** Review the results of the activity with your trainee. Be sure to have the completed assessment up on your screen or a printed copy on the table. Begin by thanking them for their efforts completing the activity. Ask them how they found the activity: Was it challenging or relatively easy to complete? About how long did it take them to complete it? Review each question, paraphrasing their responses and discussing their answers. Ask your trainee follow-up questions about their experiences with receiving and giving feedback. Depending on their past work experiences you may need to ask them questions about non-work-related feedback contexts. For example, if they have never had a formal job, consider asking them about experiences with teachers, coaches, or others in leadership positions. Ask them specific questions aimed at identifying their preferences. Whereas you can simply ask a direct question such as, "How do you prefer to receive feedback?" your trainees might be caught off guard and they might not be able to provide an informed answer. Instead, ask questions that provide some support and guidance (see examples in the side-box). Then spend some time reviewing how you will incorporate this information into your practices and asking your trainee to commit to helping you stick to that by giving you

> ## Supportive Guiding Questions
>
> - If I had some good things about your performance that I wanted to share, as well as some things that I wanted us to work on, which do think you'd like to hear about first?
>
> - How does it make you feel when someone praises you in front of others?
>
> - When you are learning something new, do you like corrective feedback in the moment as you are performing the task, or right afterwards?

feedback if you forget or slip up. For example, if your trainee says that they prefer praise to be delivered in private, you might explain that you will do your best to honor that. But, if you get overly excited and deliver some praise in front of others, you can tell your trainee that they should thank you for the praise and remind you that they prefer that praise be delivered in private.

5. **Client Related Tasks:** If there are any client-related, or other clinical tasks, that need to be assigned, you can use this time to address those items.

6. **BACB Scavenger Hunt Activity:** Spend just a few minutes finding out how much your trainee knows about the BACB and resources available on the BACB website. Do not be surprised if their knowledge is minimal; instead use this as an opportunity for rapport building and to create a brave learning environment. Think back on your early experiences. Did you know a lot about the BACB early on in your training? If not, share that story as a way to connect with your trainee and normalize not knowing things. Discuss with your trainee the purpose of licensure (particularly if you are in a licensure state) and certification entities (e.g., consumer protection, setting standard requirements for practice and professional development, providing a mechanism for submitting complaints about problematic licensee/certificant behavior, providing resources to licensees/certificants). Access the BACB website and, based on your trainee's level of knowledge and familiarity, review the main sections of the webpage. Show them the BACB Scavenger Hunt Activity in Appendix C, briefly review and answer any questions, and set a due date for completing and sharing it with you. *Note: You may wish to repeat this activity with your licensure board website, if applicable.*

7. **Wrap-Up:** End the meeting by thanking your trainee for a great conversation and for their efforts. Review any assigned tasks and due dates. Review the next meeting date and time. If needed, prompt them to have you sign any needed forms.

After Month 1 Meeting B with Your Trainee

After the second meeting with your trainee, you'll need to complete any tasks that you identified in the meeting. For example, do the following:

- Send or share any documents for assigned tasks (e.g., BACB Scavenger Hunt, assigned articles).

- Send or share meeting notes.

- Document assigned tasks and due dates so that you can collect data on timeliness (e.g., in spreadsheet, in your calendar).

- Create any needed calendar events.

- Complete the Month 1 Reflection activity.

 Month 1 Reflection Activity

Spend time reflecting on how your trainee meetings and observations went throughout Month 1 and complete the activity below. Note: you will complete this structured activity each month for review with your CS in the next meetings. Taking a structured approach to reflecting on what is going well, what needs improvements, and how you know those things will help you develop the skills related to evaluating the outcomes of your supervisory practices and facilitate you taking an active approach to making needed adjustments. It may be helpful to have brief recurring weekly time in your calendar to add information to the table throughout each month.

Month 1 Reflection

Topic/Task/ Activity	What went well and how do you know?	What could use improvements and how do you know?	What will you do differently? Questions for your CS
Rapport Building			
Reviewing Logistics			
Reviewing Contract			
Feedback Discussion			
Trainee Collaboration Activity			

👥 Month 1 Activities for Peers/CoP

- Share and discuss your histories of giving and receiving feedback. Discuss how your experiences were similar and different. How can this information help prepare you to be more responsive to your trainees?

- Share and discuss your values related to supervision. What is similar and what is different? How can this information help prepare you to be more responsive to your trainees?

- Review what each of you plan to address in the first meeting with your trainees.

- Role-play having conversations about feedback and the supervisory relationship.

- Role-play completing the Collaboration Activity for Trainees or the BACB Scavenger Hunt Activity.

- Share resources and documents (e.g., supervision tracking systems, contracts).

Congratulations! You made it through your first month!

You completed your first meeting with your CS, and you are actively planning for your first supervision meeting with your trainee! The effort that you are putting into maximizing your time with your CS and planning to support your trainee is an invaluable gift to your current trainees, their future trainees, your future trainees, and to yourself! You are well on your way to becoming the supervisor you want to be!

Month 1 Appendix A

 Collaboration Activity for Trainees

Trainee Name: _____   Due Date: _____

The purpose of this activity is to set the stage for a strong, collaborative relationship between supervisor and trainee. This activity focuses on providing you with a structured opportunity to think about and discuss topics like receiving and giving feedback and goals that you may have for yourself. You'll review this activity in a meeting with your supervisor but taking the time to think about and answer the questions should help to make the conversation more comfortable. Talking about feedback can be new to some people and can make people feel nervous. The hope is that being able to complete this on your own time will minimize you feeling put on the spot when talking about feedback and will facilitate a meaningful conversation about feedback that will help you and your supervisor start out strong. Once you are done completing this form, email or save it to a shared drive 48 hours before the meeting in which you will review it with your supervisor.

1. What are at least three things you think you are good at and are excited to show me:

    _____

    _____

    _____

2. What are at least three things you are excited to learn about during your supervised fieldwork experience?

    _____

    _____

    _____

3. What professional skills are you most excited to learn about from me during supervision? (Check all that apply.)

    ☐ organization   ☐ writing   ☐ difficult conversations

    ☐ time management   ☐ presenting   ☐ other: _____

    ☐ problem-solving   ☐ effective communication _____

(Continues on next page)

4. When you think of "feedback," what specifically, does that mean to you and how do you feel? Why? What experiences contributed to your thoughts and feelings?

    _____

    _____

    _____

5. How do you prefer to receive praise? (Check all that apply.)

    ☐ in the moment   ☐ privately   ☐ vocally (tell me)

    ☐ after the performance   ☐ in writing   ☐ I need help to figure this out

6. How do you prefer to receive corrective feedback?

    ☐ in the moment   ☐ privately   ☐ vocally (tell me)

    ☐ after the performance   ☐ in writing   ☐ I need help to figure this out

7. How comfortable are you giving me (your supervisor) direct feedback?

    ☐ pretty comfortable   ☐ nervous, but I think I can do it   ☐ scared & hesitant

    ☐ Are you kidding me? I don't even know how to answer this.

8. How do you think you would prefer to give me (your supervisor) feedback about how our supervision is going?

    ☐ Let's have a standing agenda item so we can discuss in our meetings.

    ☐ I'll send you my feedback in an email after our meetings.

    ☐ I'll just bring things up in meetings as they come up.

    ☐ I am nervous about giving you feedback and think I am going to need help with how and when to do this.

Month 1 Appendix B

Sample Trainee Tracking Form

The BACB has specific requirements for what must be documented for trainees, including documenting the accrual of overall independent hours, specific types of experience hours (e.g., restricted and unrestricted), required supervision hours, and specific types of supervision hours (e.g., individual and group). It is up to you to know about these requirements, create a fieldwork- and supervision-hours tracking system, and regularly review it with your trainee. You should also facilitate your trainee creating or using a similar tracking system. Outside of tracking hours, you should track some other things for each trainee. We recommend creating a spreadsheet with these items, as a spreadsheet will allow you to build and use dropdown menus for efficiency and consistency. You should review your tracking system with your CS each month to identify issues related to meeting the BACB requirements and to facilitate questions related to providing effective supervision (e.g., how to proceed if a skill is not being acquired, how to address skills like timeliness), as well as to review progression of hours and activities.

General Trainee Information

- Name
- Nickname
- Pronouns
- DOB (if comfortable sharing)
- Email
- Cell phone
- Name of employer and University program

- Date eligible for supervised fieldwork
- Date contract signed
- Name(s) of other supervisor (if applicable)
- Participation in group supervision?
- Type of fieldwork experience
- Anticipated BACB exam due date

Meeting/Contact Specific Information

- Date of the contact
- Start and end time
- Fieldwork type (supervised or concentrated supervised)
- Supervision type (1:1 or group)
- Format (in person or teleconsult)
- Activity category (restricted or unrestricted)
- Contact type (meeting or client observation)

- Timeliness and professionalism
- Topic of meeting/focus of observation
- Summary of activities completed
- Summary of feedback provided
- Data collected (procedural integrity, IOA, data on performance/knowledge tasks)
- Rating/Indication of progress (meeting expectations or not)

Trainee Tracking Form for Supervision with Name of Supervisor

General Trainee Information

....

Name:		DOB:	
Nickname:		Cell phone:	
Pronouns:			

| University program: | | Graduation date (actual or expected): | |

Date eligible to accrue exp. hours:	
Prior independent fieldwork hours accrued, if any:	
Prior supervised fieldwork hours accrued, if any:	
Date expected to apply to sit for BACB exam:	
Applicable BACB Task List:	

| Employer: | | Primary work setting: | |

| Other current supervisor: | | Other current supervisor: | |

Date contract signed:		Date(s) contract amended:	
Expected dates of formal reviews/assessments:	
Type of fieldwork:	
Expected average monthly independent fieldwork hours:		Expected monthly group supervision meetings/hours:	
Day/time of standing meetings/observations:	

Other Notes:

Trainee Tracking Form for Supervision with Name of Supervisor

Contact Specific Notes

General Contact Information			
Trainee:		Date:	
Start time:	End time:	Duration:	
Fieldwork type:	Supervision type:		
Format:			
Activity category:			
Contact type:			
Primary topics for meeting:			
Primary focus for observation:			

Items for Ongoing Evaluation	
On time for appointment?	
Assignments turned in on time?	
Appropriate dress for activity?	
Appropriate level of engagement in activities?	
Needed materials organized and accessible?	
Monthly Verification Form ready to be signed (if end of the month)?	

Specific Contact Information	
Summary of topics and BACB Task List items discussed:	
Summary of activities completed:	
Summary of feedback provided:	
Summary of data collected:	
Summary of overall performance against expectations	

Month 1 Appendix C

👥 BACB Scavenger Hunt Activity

Trainee Name: _____   Due Date: _____

Instructions: This activity is meant to increase your familiarity with the features and resources on the BACB website. For the activities listed below you will need to create a digital document to collect resources; for some items you will find information and write a short answer or take a screen shot and paste below or into a document that you will share with your supervisor. For other items you will need to find and download documents that you will show to your supervisor. If you already have a document, you'll still need to show your supervisor, but you can proudly say, "I already had this one!" Note: from time to time the BACB removes items for editing. If you cannot find an item, please be prepared to show your supervisor where you looked to confirm that you did not miss it.

- ☐ Find, copy, and paste the BACB's mission.

- ☐ Is the BACB a for-profit or nonprofit company?

- ☐ Find and list the names of the current Board of Directors (you don't have to list their titles).

- ☐ Find, copy, and paste the requirements to be a Subject Matter Expert.

- ☐ Find the certificate data page and list the number of BCBA certificants in the year you were born, in the current year, and in the year prior.

    - ☐ Birth Year:

    - ☐ Current Year:

    - ☐ Previous Year:

- ☐ Find and download the BACB Handbook; (review the Eligibility Requirements section for additional helpful resources) copy and paste the URL.

☐ Find and download the Tasks List that applies to your anticipated exam year; copy and paste the URL.

☐ Find and download the Supervisor Training Curriculum Outline (2.0); copy and paste the URL.

☐ Find the BACB Certificant Registry, look up your supervisor, and take a screen shot of their record (the full record after expanding it); copy and paste the image.

☐ Find and download the Ethics Code for Behavior Analysts; copy and paste the URL.

☐ Find and take a screen shot of the Self-Reporting video; copy and paste the image (extra credit if you watch it).

☐ Find and download the Self-Reporting Considerations document; copy and paste the URL.

☐ Find and take a screen shot of the form used to submit a complaint to the BACB about a BCaBA or BCBA; copy and paste the image.

☐ Find and download the Considerations for Reporting an Alleged Violation Against a BCaBA/BCBA document and the Considerations for Submitting a Notice of Alleged Violation Against an RBT document; copy and paste them.

☐ Find and list out the names of the toolkits available on the Ethics Resource page (extra credit if you download them).

☐ Find the Inside the BACB Podcast page and list the title of episodes 11 and 13 (extra credit if you listen to them).

☐ Find and take a screen shot of the BACB Newsletter page; copy and paste the image.

☐ EXTRA CREDIT: set up a BACB Gateway Account if you don't already have one. If you do, log in and take a screen shot.

Month 2
Assessing and Self-Assessing

Goals for upcoming CS meeting

- Review the outcomes and documentation from first meeting with trainees.
- Review your agendas.
- Discuss results of your self-assessment and your CS's assessment of you.
- Plan your goals and skills for months 4-6 with your CS.
- Plan for self-assessment and assessment with trainees.
- Discuss the need for culturally responsive and humble supervisory practices.

Goals for upcoming trainee meetings

- Continue the discussion about agendas.
- Introduce the importance of a competency-based approach to supervision.
- Discuss self-assessments and assessments.
- Begin to discuss cultural responsiveness and humility in supervision.

 ## Month 2 CS Meeting Activities

Before Month 2 Meeting with Your CS

Complete the following tasks in preparation for your upcoming Month 2 meeting with your CS.

PREP TASK 1 – Review Month 1 Trainee Reflection activity: Review the completed activity and prepare any points of discussion or questions for your upcoming CS meeting. Be prepared to provide your CS with your tracking documentation for your trainee's supervised fieldwork hours to ensure that everything is correct.

PREP TASK 2 – Prepare for Agenda Discussion: You and your CS discussed in your last meeting that agendas are critical for effectively managing a meeting. Review the data you collected and notes you made on your trainee agendas and prepare any questions you may have for your CS.

PREP TASK 3 – Review Self-Assessment and Goals: Review your completed New Supervisor Self-Assessment Foundational Supervision Skills and draft goals that you completed in the Getting Ready section. If needed, make additional notes, and revise your self-assessment and draft goals. After reviewing your self-assessment and goals, take a look at the skills-specific section to identify what areas are best matched with your needs. Review and prioritize your goals and related skills to be addressed based on foundational skills and skills that you will need to use right away with your trainees. If you make substantial changes, make sure that you let your CS know and make the updated version available to them (e.g., email or upload new versions) before your Month 2 CS meeting.

PREP TASK 4 – Prepare Self-Assessment and Initial Assessments for Trainees: In addition to reviewing your self-assessment with your CS, you will discuss how to introduce the topic of self-assessments with your trainees in your Month 2 supervision meetings. If your company provides you with self-assessments and assessments to use with trainees make sure that you save a copy in the shared-file system. If your company only provides an assessment, and not a self-assessment, consider the edits you could make to the assessment tool to make it suitable for use as a self-assessment and begin making those revisions. If you do not have an assessment or self-assessment available, use the resources you have compiled to identify and review one or more options. For example, you can use the BCBA®/BCaBA® 5th Edition Task List Self-Assessment by Tagg and Biagi (2020) that is printed in the appendix of the LeBlanc et al. (2020) supervision book for having the trainee self-assess, then you can use the same content to conduct your own assessment. Alternatively, you could create your own in a document or spreadsheet using the items from the BACB Task List and other relevant skill areas (e.g., problem-solving, organization, time management, behavioral-skills training).

Checklist for Preparing for CS Month 2 Meeting

- ☐ Review the Month 1 Reflection activity and prepare fieldwork tracking documentation.

- ☐ Review the agendas you used in Month 1 with your trainees.

- ☐ Review and, if needed, update and re-send self-assessment and draft goals.

- ☐ Prepare draft assessment and self-assessment for trainee.

- ☐ Prepare the Consulting Supervision Documentation form.

1. **Review Trainee Meetings and Observations**: Provide a summary of how your first month of supervision meetings, activities, and observations went with your trainees. Use the information from the Month 1 Reflection activity to highlight things that went particularly well and discuss areas for improvement. Share your ideas for what you might do differently next time and make notes of suggestions from your CS. Show your CS your tracking documentation for your trainee's supervised fieldwork hours. If you and your CS identify any errors or concerns, make a to-do list of needed changes and follow-up tasks. Plan to make any revisions to the Month 1 trainee materials and activities over the course of the coming months while the information is still fresh in your mind. This will set you up for success with your next round of trainees.

   Notes: _____

   _____

   _____

2. **Agenda Discussion**: Review your assessment of the agendas you created and used with your trainees, discussing how they were helpful, and how accurate your time estimates were. As you continue to create and evaluate agendas for meetings with trainees, your CS, and others look for commonalities between items or tasks that you tend to over or underestimate and do your best to adjust your estimates moving forward for similar items or tasks.

   Notes: _____

   _____

   _____

3. **Review Your Self-Assessment and Goals**: Your CS will have reviewed your self-assessment results and have conducted some degree of assessing your skills during your pre-meeting and Month 1 meetings and the tasks you have completed up to this point. When reviewing your self-assessment, expect your CS to talk to you about any disconnects they have detected between your self-assessment and their assessment of your skills. You will also identify the content to be covered in Month 4 through Month 6 in your monthly CS meetings. We can't tell you which specific skills you'll need when because you are unique and ever-changing. However, you and your CS can identify the skills you need for the next few months. The first half of the year will likely focus on honing your basic supervision skills, whereas the second half (which you will plan with your CA later) generally will focus on advanced skills. Your CS will create a Yearly Planning Guide/Roadmap and share it with you (a blank copy is provided for you in Month 2 Appendix A). Keep in mind that this will be a flexible plan that can be reviewed and reordered if needed. You will plug the skill-specific content into the Month 4-11 templates to build out tasks for each month using the same format of 1) preparing for your CS meeting, 2) during your CS meeting, 3) to do after your CS meeting, 4) preparing for your trainee meetings, 5) during your trainee meetings, and 6) to do after your trainee meetings. Some months will have prompts for specific actions or activities (e.g., re-doing the Workload Assessment, obtaining formal feedback from your trainees, completing skills assessment).

4. **Discuss Assessments and Self-Assessments for Trainees**: Your CS will facilitate a conversation about the importance of self-assessment and assessments for trainees. You will have a similar conversation with your trainees, so pay careful attention to how your CS frames the discussion. Show your CS the self-assessment and assessment resources that you have and identify any needed edits.

   Notes: _____

   _____

   _____

5. **Discuss Culturally Responsive and Humble Practices**: Your CS will facilitate a conversation describing cultural responsiveness and humility. Your CS will also cover culturally responsive and humble strategies you can engage in during your supervisory activities. You will draft scripts for having a similar discussion with your trainees, as well as tasks to include in your supervisory practices. For example, you can make sure that you pronounce your trainee's names correctly; name your pronouns; ask your trainee their pronouns; endeavor to use diverse examples and include work from diverse authors; create space to discuss diversity, equity, and inclusion. For more information on these topics, consider reviewing the article by Wright (2019) and Chapter 4 in the Le Blanc et al. (2020) supervision book. Your CS may assign you the Self-Reflection on Culturally Responsive and Humble Practices (Appendix B) to complete, along with other self-reflection activities. It is okay if this content is new to you and/or causes some discomfort. Remember that discomfort is an indicator of a growth opportunity. If you find this content particularly challenging or interesting, you can ask your CS for additional reading to explore.

   Notes: _____

   _____

   _____

6. **Wrap-Up**: Review assigned tasks and/or readings and due dates. Confirm date and time of next meeting. Ask your CS to sign the Consulting Supervision Document form.

After Month 2 Meeting with Your CS

Review and complete the following activities:

- Receive your Months 4-6 Yearly Planning Guide/Roadmap from your CS and save it.
- Trainee Supervised Fieldwork Documentation: Calendar time to complete any edits to your documentation system and complete any follow-up tasks.
- Month 1 Trainee Revisions: Make a list of needed revision to your Month 1 trainee materials and activities and calendar time to make any needed revisions over the next two months.
- Self-Reflection on Culturally Responsive and Humble Practices: Complete the self-reflection activity in Appendix B to help you prepare for beginning this discussion on the topic with your trainees and to review with your CS in Month 3. Broad questions to consider before and after the activity, as well as regularly throughout your career include the following:
  - Where are you, in terms of being culturally responsive and humble?
  - How do culturally responsive and humble supervisory practices connect to your values?
  - What culturally responsive and humble practices do you engage in during supervision and clinical work?

MONTH 2 TRAINEE MEETING ACTIVITIES

Before Month 2 Meeting with Your Trainee

Complete the following tasks in preparation of your upcoming Month 2 meetings and observations with your trainees. In Month 1 we provided two outlines, one for Month 1 Meeting A and another one for Meeting B. However, moving forward it will be up to you to decide how to spread the presented topics and content across several meetings and observations, as the BACB requires multiple contacts each month. You can discuss how to split these activities across your trainee meetings as appropriate for the time scheduled and the needs present in each meeting with your CS.

PREP TASK 1 – Prepare Meeting and Observation Agendas: Make agendas for upcoming meetings and observations in Month 2. Include time to check in and review how things went in Month 1. Include the following standing items on your agenda:

- **Client Related Topics/Tasks:** Make an outline of any items for discussion or training related to clients. Be sure to gather any needed materials (e.g., data sheets, instructional materials, program descriptions/protocols, procedural integrity checklists).

- **BACB Task List/Behavior-Analytic Topics/Tasks:** Make an outline of any specific knowledge or skills to cover. It is a good idea to include the related ethics standards for each topic or skill you cover. Be sure to gather any needed materials (e.g., training stimuli, role-play scripts, video examples).

PREP TASK 2 – Review Meeting and Observation Notes: Look back over the notes from your meetings, observations, and product reviews (if relevant) to prepare for the upcoming meeting.

PREP TASK 3 – Prepare Other Topics/Tasks – Agenda Discussion and Expectations: Reflect on and prepare your continued discussion about the importance of agendas for effective meetings. If you are going to have a standing-agenda item where the trainees can add in client-specific questions or topics, plan to talk about your expectations for things like how much information should be included (shoot for requiring a few descriptive words or phrases over just client initials or long descriptions) and by when the items should be added to the agenda (e.g., at least 24 hours before the meeting).

PREP TASK 4 – Prepare Other Topics/Tasks – Simple, Initial Self-Assessment/Assessment: Create a simple, initial self-assessment/assessment to give to your trainee. Several options are available for creating this assessment/self-assessment. Perhaps your organization already has one for you to use. If you do not have one, consider using the one created by Biagi and Tagg that is included in the LeBlanc, Sellers et al. (2020) book. You could also use some of the more basic or foundational items from the BACB Task List. You will use the same items for the trainee to self-assess and for you to assess based on the activities completed in your meetings and from your observations. Prepare a script or outline for

1. discussing the importance of conducting self-assessments,
2. describing the expectations for the trainee to complete the self-assessment, and
3. explaining that you will review it later in the month to discuss the results and compare them with the results of the assessments you have been completing.

Consider linking self-assessments and assessments to the BACB ethics standards around assessing for scope of competence, assessing for personal biases, and evaluating the outcomes of clinical programming and supervision. If the self-assessment is ready before the meeting with your trainee, consider making it available for them to review.

PREP TASK 5 – Prepare Other Topics/Tasks—Culturally Responsive And Humble Practices Scripts: Draft scripts for beginning to discuss culturally responsive and humble practices, both in supervision and clinical practices. Review the related BACB ethics standards in preparation for this discussion. For more information, review Wright's 2019 article and Chapter 4 in the book by LeBlanc, Sellers et al. (2020).

⬚ Checklist for Preparing for Trainee Month 2 Meetings

- ☐ Create meeting and observation agendas.

- ☐ Review notes from meetings and observations.

- ☐ Prep for agenda discussion.

- ☐ Prepare assessment/self-assessment and plan for discussion.

- ☐ Prepare for culturally responsive and humble discussion.

During Month 2 Meeting with Your Trainee

1. **Check In:** Take a few minutes to greet your trainee and check in on how they are doing. Review the agenda with them and ask if there are any pressing clinical needs to add.

2. **Review Last Meeting:** Review any standing items or tasks that were assigned from the last meeting and are due in this meeting. Remember that due dates for tasks will span across the multiple meetings with your trainees, so use your tracking system to make sure you are addressing the correct tasks due in a given meeting.

3. **Review Observations and Products:** Review any items that you noted from your observations and product reviews, if relevant. If needed, provide training.

4. **Client-Related Tasks:** Discuss any client-specific tasks (e.g., introducing a new program, reviewing data).

5. **BACB Task List/Behavior-Analytic Topics/Tasks:** Introduce any new concepts or skills related to the Task List or other relevant behavior-analytic content. You might also use this time to continue working on content or skills that are complex and require multiple meetings to cover. Be sure to document specific content covered, progress, and feedback in your tracking system.

6. **Other Topics/Tasks – Agenda Discussion:** Spend just a few minutes on the function of agendas in supporting effective meetings (e.g., manage and respect time, prioritize topics). Use this as an opportunity to set the stage for bi-directional feedback. Tell your trainee that you are going to ask for their feedback about the structure of the agenda and if they have any recommended changes to make the agenda more effective for the two of you. If you are going to allow your trainee to add client-specific agenda items, discuss the expectations and let them know that you will give them feedback about whether the language they use needs any adjusting in the future.

7. **Other Topics/Tasks – Assessments/Self-Assessments:** Introduce the topic of assessments and self-assessments and facilitate a discussion about their function, how you use them yourself (i.e., self-assessments that you conduct, assessments that your CS conducts of your performance), and how you will use them in your supervision of your trainee. Show them the assessment/self-assessment tool that you use, explain how to complete it, and tell them when it is done (likely in your last meeting in Month 2). Make sure to ask if they have any questions and consider testing for comprehension by having them describe the purpose and expectations back to you.

8. **Other Topics/Tasks – Culturally Responsive and Humble Practices:** Have a brief conversation introducing the terms and concepts of culturally responsive practice and cultural humility, in relation to supervisory and clinical practices. This conversation should be brief, as it should be woven into almost all clinical content, and into supervision-specific discussions.

9. **Wrap-Up:** Wrap up the meeting by thanking your trainee for their continued efforts and participation in the meetings. Review assigned tasks (e.g., adding client-specific items to the agenda, client-specific tasks, Task List tasks, and completing the self-assessment), tasks due dates, and the upcoming observations and meetings for the remainder of Month 2. If needed, prompt them to have you sign any needed forms.

After Month 2 Meeting(s) with Your Trainee

Carry out any follow-up tasks from the meeting with your trainee and plan for other meetings and observations that will take place with your trainee during the month.

- Send or make available the self-assessment.
- Send any materials for other tasks (e.g., articles to read).
- Send or post meeting notes.
- Complete Month 2 Reflection activity.

Month 2 Reflection Activity

Topic/Task/Activity	What went well and how do you know?	What could use improvements and how do you know?	What will you do differently? Questions for your CS
Check in			
Agenda Discussion			
Assessment and Self-Assessment Discussion			
Self-Assessment Activity			
Culturally Responsive and Humble Practices: Discussion			

👥 MONTH 2 ACTIVITIES FOR PEERS/CoP

- Share and discuss how things have gone over your second month of meeting with your CS and trainees. Discuss how your experiences are similar and different.

- Share your agendas/observation templates and discuss how the use of agendas has supported effective meetings and anything you have learned about how to best structure and talk about agendas with your trainees.

- Discuss how your self-assessment discussion went with your CS. Discuss the goals you are developing for yourself. How are your self-assessment results and goals similar or different?

- Share and discuss the assessment/self-assessment tool you are going to use with your trainees.

- Role-play having conversations about assessment and self-assessments.

- Discuss what *cultural responsiveness* and *cultural humility* mean to you. If anyone has read any articles or book chapters, share them, and discuss. If you all are comfortable, begin having an open discussion about your personal biases and strategies you are implementing to be culturally responsive and humble in your supervisory and clinical practices.

- Role-play conversations about culturally responsive and humble practices.

- Share resources and documents (e.g., tools, tracking systems, articles).

Making it to this point means that you have made it through your first two months of supervising. That is no small feat! If you are feeling overwhelmed, that's okay! Providing high-quality supervision to your trainees, while simultaneously working to increase your own supervision repertoires and making sure that clients are getting excellent clinical services requires a lot of thoughtful planning and effort. You should be really proud of yourself. Maybe everything didn't go quite as planned; that's perfectly normal! If this author shared all her mistakes and failed plans, this workbook would be epically long. Make sure that you are taking care of yourself by managing your stress levels, getting enough sleep, eating well, and doing things you love. You are critically important to the success of your clients, trainees, and the profession in general, so take good care of YOU!

Month 2 Appendix A

Yearly Planning Guide/Roadmap

	Your Initials:		**Your CS's Initials:**		
Month 1	Starting strong	Starting strong	Starting strong	Starting strong	Starting strong
Month 2	Assessing and self-assessing	Assessing and self-assessing	Assessing and self-assessing	Assessing and self-assessing	Assessing and self-assessing
Month 3	Circular roadmap and competencies	Circular roadmap and competencies	Circular roadmap and competencies	Circular roadmap and competencies	Circular roadmap and competencies
Month 4					
Month 5					
Month 6					
Month 7					
Month 8					
Month 9					
Month 10					
Month 11					
Month 12					

Month 2 Appendix B

Self-Reflection on Culturally Responsive and Humble Practices

Self-reflection and self-assessment, particularly related to this content, should be a regular part of your professional experience as a behavior analyst. The following questions are meant to assist you in identifying any potential negative, implicit biases that you may hold, along with identifying how many of your practices are consistently culturally responsive and humble. Some of the reflection questions may make you feel uncomfortable, and that is all right. Do your best to be honest and kind to yourself as you explore these topics. It is best to engage with these self-reflection questions under optimal conditions. For example, plan to review them during a time when you are not rushed or overly tired. Consider creating an environment to maximize thoughtful reflection such as playing soft music, making a cup of tea or glass of iced water, and sitting near a window for some natural light. You do not have to complete the entire list of self-reflection items all at once. It is fine to complete the content over a few reflection sessions.

Items for General Self-Reflection

1. I sometimes assume that people have bad intentions based on race, culture, religion, gender identity, sexual preference or other identity variable.

2. I generally assume that others share my values and preferences.

3. I am uncomfortable when people express their emotions around me.

4. I generally spend time with those who share my religious, cultural, and racial identity.

5. I sometimes fail to recognize my own privilege, power, and advantage compared to others.

6. I can fluently describe my cultural identity to others.

7. I consider my communication style more consistent with—

    a. Low context – often rely on explicit and direct, verbal instructions; equal control of conversational exchanges by communication partners; privacy and respect for personal space.

    b. High context – often rely on contextual cues and stories to direct behavior; voice tone, facial expressions, and other physical cues; allot differential importance and time to communication partners; and valuing of communal space.

8. I regularly seek new experiences to learn about other cultures.

9. I have voluntarily enrolled in a cultural competency and responsiveness training course.

10. I am involved in a community of practice that is dedicated to inclusion and fairness.

11. I do not knowingly engage in behavior that is harassing or demeaning to persons based on their gender identity, gender expression, or gendered preferences, interests, or behaviors.

12. I am committed to TGNC-affirming practices.

13. My behavior-analytic practices and professional activities actively challenge power imbalances for marginalized communities.

Items for Self-Reflection Specific to Supervision and Clinical Work

1. I consider any cultural differences with my trainees or clients and ask about culturally important variables (e.g., asking open-ended questions, learning about comfortable communication styles, asking about the conditions for respect and inclusion, asking about the meaning assigned to important events for the trainee or client).

2. I consider the social and economic barriers that might impact a trainee's ability to maximize their fieldwork experiences or a client's ability to receive care.

3. I ask kind, open-ended, forthright questions about culture, identity, or potential differences of my trainees and clients.

4. I develop plans for addressing any significant power differentials that exist in supervisory and client relationships.

5. I identify and address various factors (e.g., cultural and religious, SES, ethnicity, race, sexuality, language barriers, and gender roles) that might impact my relationship with my trainees or clients.

6. I directly talk about privilege and disadvantage with my trainees.

7. I feel comfortable engaging in "skilled dialogues" which involve welcoming, sense-making, appreciating, allowing, joining, and harmonizing.

8. I feel comfortable with trainees and clients expressing emotions in a variety of different ways.

9. I am aware of the religious practices of my trainees and clients, and I try to act in ways that are respectful of their practices.

10. I make space for trainees and clients to name their own identities if they wish.

11. I have considered how my own cultural identities shape my worldview and potentially hinder my connections to trainees and clients.

12. When conducting preference assessments or reinforcer assessments, I include items typically associated with all genders available for all clients.

13. I make sure that the stimuli that I use in training and intervention are culturally and racially anchored and inclusive.

14. I actively address inequalities experienced by my supervisees or clients.

Month 3

Curricular Roadmap and Competencies

<table>
<tr>
<td>

Goals for upcoming CS meeting

- Review outcomes of Month 2 supervision activities with trainees.
- Complete your goals with your CS.
- Plan for taking over the agenda.
- Plan for outlining competencies and goal setting with trainees.

</td>
<td>

Goals for upcoming trainee meetings

- Review trainees' self-assessment and your assessment of them.
- Begin to identify goals and plan content for coming months.
- Continue to establish importance of agendas and identify agenda tasks for the trainee in Month 4.
- Continue to discuss culturally responsive and humble practices.
- Solicit formal feedback from your trainee.

</td>
</tr>
</table>

 Month 3 CS Meeting Activities

Before Month 3 Meeting with Your CS

Complete the following tasks in preparation of your upcoming Month 3 meeting with your CS.

PREP TASK 1 – Complete the Month 2 Trainee Reflection activity: Spend time reflecting on how your trainee meetings and observations went throughout Month 2 and complete the activity on the following page.

PREP TASK 2 – Soliciting Formal Feedback from Trainee: Review or create a feedback form that you will give to your trainee in Months 3, 6, 9, and 12, and then at regular intervals until your supervision ends. We provide a sample feedback form that you can use as is or modify (Appendix A). You can also review the feedback form created by Turner et al. (2016) that is reprinted in the supervision and mentorship book by LeBlanc et al. (2020). Decide if the feedback will be collected directly or anonymously, which will not be possible if you have only one trainee and may be difficult if you have only two. If you are collecting the feedback anonymously and using a form that will be filled out and returned, decide how to collect them (e.g., have them complete the form on their computer, print, and drop in a box or give to someone who will then pass them to you; use an online anonymous option like Survey Monkey). Think about how you will introduce this to your trainee (e.g., "This is a chance for me to improve my supervisory skills, which I value greatly.") Prepare any questions you have for your CS.

Notes: _____

_____

_____

PREP TASK 3 – Review Your Goals and Skills for Months 4-6: Review the goals and skills that you and your CS agreed on for the coming months. If you feel that any of these need to be modified, be prepared to discuss with your CS. If you made revisions to the goals or have proposed revisions to the Month 4-6 content, send that to your CS before the Month 3 meeting.

PREP TASK 4 – Workload Assessment Re-Do: Complete the Workload Assessment activity again. Once it is completed, compare it to the one you completed in the Getting Ready section. Email or share the results with your CS and be prepared to review in the upcoming meeting with your CS.

Workload Assessment Month 3

Task	Average Weekly Time Requirement	Facilitators	Barriers
Client caseload management			
RBT caseload			
BCaBA caseload			
Trainee caseload			
Administrative responsibilities			
Other duties			
Total average weekly work hours:			

PREP TASK 5 – Culturally Responsive and Humble Practices: Review how your brief, initial discussion about this topic went with your trainees. Was the conversation uncomfortable for you? Were you able to detect that your trainee was uncomfortable? Did your trainee have any questions for which you felt unprepared? Thinking about these things and preparing questions for your CS will not only support continued discussions with your current trainees but will facilitate increased fluency and comfort in bringing up the topic with new trainees. Review the results from your Self-Reflection on Culturally Responsive and Humble Practices Activity. Did this activity bring up any questions or concerns for you? Develop questions for your CS.

Notes: _____

_____

_____

PREP TASK 6 – Trainee Assessment and Self-Assessment: Review the results from your ongoing assessment of your trainees and their self-assessment (if they have completed it). Think about how you will address reviewing the results and discussing areas of strength and growth with your trainees and prepare questions for your CS. If preparing scripts has been helpful, draft a few that you can review and use to role-play with your CS.

Notes: _____

_____

_____

PREP TASK 7 – Trainee Curricular Roadmap and Competencies: Based on the results of your assessments and observations of your trainees, as well as their self-assessment, begin to draft a roadmap of content you will cover with them, restricted and unrestricted activities, and specific competencies that will be used to determine mastery for the content and skills. Link the content to items from the BACB Task List, Ethics Code for Behavior Analysts (2020), and Supervisor Training Curriculum (2.0) (BACB, 2018). Be sure to include other relevant skills necessary to be a successful, independent clinician (e.g., interpersonal communication, problem-solving, time management). You will review this roadmap with your CS this month. You might consider creating a table or spreadsheet to arrange and track the content and skills. Below is an example:

Content or Skill	Restricted Activities	Unrestricted Activities	Criteria for Competency	Related Task List Item(s)	Related Ethics Code Standard(s)	Related Supervisor Training Curriculum (2.0) Items

Notes: _____

_____

_____

☑️ Checklist for Preparing for CS Month 3 Meeting

- ☐ Review your self-assessment and CS assessment of you.

- ☐ Revise your goals and send/share with CS.

- ☐ Prepare your Consulting Supervision Documentation form.

- ☐ Review your assessment of trainees and their self-assessment.

- ☐ Review notes re: Culturally Responsive and Humble practice discussion and your self-assessment.

- ☐ Prepare a formal-feedback form.

- ☐ Complete the Month 3 Workload Assessment and send/share with CS.

During Month 3 Meeting with Your CS

1. Review Trainee Meetings and Observations: During your meeting you will have a chance to provide a brief summary of how things are going with your trainees and discuss any issues or questions with your CS.

2. Review Plan for Soliciting Feedback from Trainees: During the meeting your CS will want to hear your plan for having the conversation with your trainees about formal feedback and the value of them providing feedback to you about your supervisory practices. Your CS will also ask about the strategies you plan to use for soliciting feedback from your trainees and see any forms or surveys you have developed.

3. Review Your Goals and Yearly Planning Guide/Roadmap for Months 4-6: Your CS will check in to see if you have any remaining questions or revisions to the plan laid out in the last meeting. Expect your CS to check in on the plan regularly. If you are struggling with a skill of your own or one you are teaching to your trainee, you need to bring it up with your CS for support. This is true even if it is a skill that you have previously covered, or one that you have planned to occur in a future month. Your CS will appreciate your self-reflection and ability to ask for support.

4. Review Workload Assessment: In preparation for this month, you revisited your Workload Assessment. Your CS will ask for an update about the results and any needs you identified.

5. Review Discussion About Culturally Responsive and Humble Practices: Your CS will check in on how the conversation went, so be prepared to provide a summary, and discuss how to continue to facilitate weaving this content into your supervisory (and clinical) practices.

   Notes: _____

   _____

   _____

6. Review Assessment/Self-Assessment for Trainees: Review how the conversation went with your trainees and review the results of your assessments of your trainees. If you have identified any areas of significant concern, discuss with your CS. If your trainees have completed their self-assessment, review it with your CS discussing any areas of disconnect between results (i.e., between how you and your trainee evaluated their skills). If needed, role-play conversations for addressing the results with your trainees. If you predict that your trainee might respond in a certain way (e.g., disagree with your assessment, become upset or overly self-critical) be sure to ask your CS to practice ways to respond.

   Notes: _____

   _____

   _____

7. Reviewing Curricular Roadmap and Competencies for Trainees: Your CS will ask you to share the draft roadmap for the content and skills you plan on addressing with your trainees. Discuss with them the match between the assessment results and the topics you have planned out and identify any needed revisions.

8. Agendas: Your CS will discuss how agendas can be used as a learning opportunity for you and a teaching tool with your trainees. As you have the discussion, take notes about how you will discuss agendas with your trainees and the steps you will take to leverage them as teaching tools. Your CS will describe their expectations for you in Month 4 as you take responsibility of preparing and managing the agendas for your CS meetings. Similarly, in your Month 4 meetings with your trainees, you will continue your conversations about agendas and discuss that you are going to give them some ownership over the meeting agenda. For your trainees you will take a slower approach (e.g., asking them to add client concerns and celebrations for one to two months, asking them to nominate topics or skills to address or evaluate in the next few months, and so on) to this than your CS will take with you. Discuss your ideas for how you will begin to assign your trainees tasks related to managing the agenda over time and how you will introduce this topic.

   Notes: _____

   _____

   _____

9. Wrap-Up: Review assigned tasks and/or readings and due dates. Confirm the date and time of the next meeting. Ask your CS to sign the Consulting Supervision Document form.

After Month 3 Meeting with Your CS

Review and complete the following activities:

- Make any needed revisions to your feedback scripts.
- Make any needed revisions to your trainee roadmaps.
- Schedule time to develop the agenda for your Month 4 CS meeting by the due date.

🏃 Month 3 Trainee Meeting and Observation Activities

Before Month 3 Meetings with Your Trainee

Complete the following tasks in preparation for your upcoming Month 3 meetings and observations with your trainees. Remember that these activities should be spread across several meetings and observations, as the BACB requires multiple contacts each month. It is up to you to split these activities across your trainee meetings as appropriate for the time schedule and the needs present in each meeting.

PREP TASK 1 – Prepare Meeting and Observation Agendas: Continue to refine your meeting and observation agendas based on notes you have taken.

1. Client Related Topics/Tasks: _____

_____

_____

2. BACB Task List/Behavior Analytic Topics/Tasks: _____

_____

_____

PREP TASK 2 – Review Meeting and Observation Notes: Review your notes from meetings, observations, and other tasks/products and plan any follow-up activities (e.g., additional training, scheduling time for trainee to observe you or others).

PREP TASK 3 – Prepare Other Topics/Tasks – Review Assessment and Self-Assessment: Based on your discussion with your CS, review any scripts or notes to prepare for discussing the assessments with your trainees.

PREP TASK 4 – Prepare Other Topics/Tasks – Discuss Goals and Competency-Based Tasks: Prepare your conversation for identifying goals for your trainees, mapping out the content you will cover during the supervisor relationship, and the importance of using a competency-based approach (i.e., pre-identified mastery criteria that include generalization and maintenance). Providing a full curriculum of behavior-analytic and BACB Task List content to cover during your trainees' supervised fieldwork experience is beyond the scope of this workbook. Be sure to plan ways that you can solicit ideas and preferences from your trainees for goals and topics/tasks to include. Revisit and revise the month-to-month outline of BACB Task List, ethics, and other topics and skills you will address. Remember, there should be a progression from foundational, direct activities in a specific area moving toward independence and indirect activities as your trainees demonstrate mastery. This topic should be addressed in all your meetings with your trainees during Month 3. If you meet with your trainees twice you should introduce the topic and share a few of your goals for your trainees in the first meeting. Then, you can assign the task of drafting a few goals and topics/tasks of interest for themselves that they can share with you in your second meeting. In the second meeting you can review what the trainee has identified and share your outline for the coming months and the specifics of how you will assess and determine mastery.

PREP TASK 5 – Agendas: Outline how you will begin to assign tasks related to prepping and managing the agenda. Here is one possible approach:

- Start by having them take notes during the meeting and sharing or emailing them by a certain deadline (e.g., within 24 hours of the meeting). Collect data on things like timeliness, accuracy of the notes, and responsiveness to feedback (if needed).

- Once they are managing the notes well, consider increasing the expectations. The next step might be to have them manage creating a new agenda (using a template) for upcoming meetings by a certain deadline (e.g., 48 hours before the meeting) and adding specific items (e.g., indicating some behavior-analytic content they would like to cover or for which they are ready to be assessed, client-specific celebrations or challenges, ethics scenarios or questions). Continue taking data on the same variables but consider adding information about how well they appear to be prioritizing topics or needs.

- As they demonstrate success at this level of agenda management, you can decide to turn more ownership over to them until they are independently managing the agenda and you are simply adding items that you need to cover. Using this systematic, competency-based approach, you will gain insight into their organization and time-management skills and provide feedback (praise and corrective) as needed.

PREP TASK 6 – Prepare Other Topics/Tasks – Formal Feedback: Prepare the formal-feedback activity. Make sure you have the feedback form or link to the online anonymous survey ready to share with your trainees and a due date for completing it. Review the notes from the discussion with your CS and revise or prep any needed scripts or points for discussion. Ultimately, you want to create a culture of continual bi-directional feedback and clearly communicate to your trainees that the feedback they provide to you is critical for you to continue to improve your supervisory skills and to ensure that you can create a successful experience for them.

☷ Checklist for Preparing for Trainee Month 3 Meetings

- ☐ Create meeting and observation agendas.

- ☐ Review notes from meetings and observations.

- ☐ Review your assessments of your trainee.

- ☐ Review trainees' self-assessment. (If they did not complete it by the due date, provide immediate feedback and the expectation to have it completed by a specific date.)

- ☐ Prep your expectations for your trainee related to the agenda.

- ☐ Prep the formal feedback from trainee activity.

During Month 3 Meetings with Your Trainee

The following items should be covered in your trainee meetings across Month 3. Some of the items should occur in each meeting (e.g., check in, review last meeting, review observations and products). It is up to you to determine in which meetings the other items should occur.

1. **Check In:**

2. **Review Last Meeting:**

3. **Review Observations and Products:**

4. **Client Related Tasks:**

5. **BACB Task List/ Behavior-Analytic Topics/Tasks:**

6. **Other Topics/Tasks – Review Assessment and Self-Assessment:** Spend time reviewing their self-assessment and your assessment. Discuss the purpose of self-assessments which includes 1) being able to self-observe and assess, 2) being able to assess and determine one's scope of competence, 3) modeling quality supervision skills of assessing before beginning to teach. Take time to call out specific items with good correspondence

Examples for Addressing Disconnects

- You rated yourself lower/higher than I did for item X. Why do you think that might be?

- Are you typically very self-critical/ overly confident?

- Are there specific areas that you consistently feel you underperform/ overperform, but for which you don't actually have data to support that assessment?

- Let's work on frequently checking in on how we each think you have done on X with a particular eye toward building your ability to accurately evaluate your performance and related confidence level.

between you and the trainee, as well as those with a disconnect. Disconnects could result from the trainee rating their performance below your assessment. Alternatively, the disconnect could go in the other direction—your trainee may have indicated that they are more skilled than you have detected. Have a conversation about the nature of the disconnect and how you will address it together. See the side box for some examples of how you can have this conversation.

7. **Other Topics/Tasks – Discuss Goals and Competency-Based Tasks:** The conversations about goals and competency-based tasks and assessment will likely take place across several meetings this month and in Month 4. Focus on creating a collaborative approach to identifying goals and content to cover and clearly indicate that you want the trainee to take an active role in directing their supervised, fieldwork experience. Include content from the goals they have shared for themselves for their career by highlighting related content you will include.

8. **Other Topics/Tasks – Agenda Tasks:** Continue the conversation about agendas based on the discussions you have had with your CS. Introduce the idea that you want to use the meeting agendas as a training opportunity for them; as being organized, managing time, and running effective meetings are critical skills for clinicians and supervisors and can minimize stressors. Describe your expectations for them related to the agenda starting in Month 4.

9. **Other Topics/Tasks – Formal Feedback from Trainees' Activity:** Continue your discussion about feedback and the importance of bi-directional feedback using the scripts and discussion points you prepared. Show them the formal-feedback activity, review the items, and answer any questions. Clearly review the expectations for how they should complete the activity (e.g., using the link, completing the form on their computer, printing it, and to whom they should give the form; completing it and emailing or posting to a shared folder) and a due date.

10. **Wrap Up:** Review the upcoming tasks, due dates, and meetings/observations during Month 3. Review the agenda task and due date for Month 4. If needed, prompt them to have you sign any needed forms.

After Month 3 Meetings with Your Trainee

Carry out any follow-up tasks from the meeting with your trainee and plan for other meetings and observations that will take place with your trainee during the month.

- Send any materials for other tasks (e.g., articles to read).
- Send or post meeting notes.
- Send Formal Feedback for Trainee document or link.
- Schedule a reminder to check on completion of the agenda task for Month 4.
- Complete Month 3 Trainee Reflection activity.

Month 3 Reflection Activity

Topic/Task/ Activity	What went well and how do you know?	What could use improvements and how do you know?	What will you do differently? Questions for your CS

👥 Month 3 Activities for Peers/CoP

- Share and discuss how things have gone over your third month of meeting with your CS and trainees. Discuss how your experiences are similar and different.

- Discuss how you are going to manage the agenda for your CS meetings and share templates.

- Discuss how you are going to use the trainee agenda as a teaching opportunity and share your plan for systematically increasing the expectations for your trainee to manage the agenda over the coming months.

- Discuss how your goals have evolved since the "Getting Ready" activities and review your month-to-month plans with your CS.

- Discuss your workload re-assessment.

- Share the outcomes of your trainees' self-assessment and your assessment of them. Discuss how the conversation went. Did others have similar experiences with any disconnects identified?

- Share competency-based tasks and activities.

- Role-play how to talk about the formal-feedback activity. Discuss how the formal-feedback discussion went and if the feedback included areas for your improvement. If so, how will you address this with your trainees and what steps will you take to implement the feedback?

- Discuss your self-care activities and support each other with setting goals for stress management and self-care.

Month 3 Appendix A

Soliciting Formal Feedback from Trainee

Always = 3   Usually = 2   Never = 1

If an item is not applicable strike through the scoring numbers and skip it. Place an "X" in the "Specific Feedback" column if you provided specific feedback about this item in the notes section.

Item	Score			Specific Feedback?
1. Supervisor is timely (e.g., arriving for meetings, meeting due dates).	3	2	1	
2. Supervisor follows through on tasks.	3	2	1	
3. Supervisor provides clear expectations of tasks and due dates.	3	2	1	
4. Supervisor creates a collaborative relationship.	3	2	1	
5. Supervisor demonstrates culturally responsive and humble practices.	3	2	1	
6. Supervisor is actively engaged in meetings and observations.	3	2	1	
7. Supervisor treats me with respect and dignity.	3	2	1	
8. Supervisor treats mistakes as learning opportunities.	3	2	1	
9. Supervisor provides the opportunity to ask questions and provides full answers.	3	2	1	
10. Supervisor solicits feedback regularly.	3	2	1	
11. Supervisor engages in high-quality, feedback-reception skills.	3	2	1	
12. Supervisor implements feedback that I have provided.	3	2	1	
13. Supervisor delivers high-quality feedback (e.g., behavior specific).	3	2	1	
14. Supervisor reviews written products (e.g., reports, protocols, emails).	3	2	1	
15. Supervisor documents activities and feedback.	3	2	1	
16. Supervisor implements high-quality instruction (e.g., BST).	3	2	1	
17. Supervisor uses a competency-based approach to teaching me.	3	2	1	
18. Supervisor addresses behavior-analytic content and items from the BACB Task List.	3	2	1	
19. Supervisor covers ethics content.	3	2	1	
20. Supervisor includes other content linked to success as a clinician and future supervisor (e.g., organization and time management, interpersonal communication, problem-solving).	3	2	1	
21. Supervisor makes space for addressing self-care and stress management.	3	2	1	
22. Supervisor facilitates my ability to make clinical decisions.	3	2	1	
23. Supervisor facilitates my professional development.	3	2	1	
TOTAL:				

List three things that your supervisor consistently does well:

1. _____

2. _____

3. _____

List three things on which my supervisor could improve (this could be increasing consistency or quality, doing more of something, doing less of something, adding in something they currently are not doing):

1. _____

2. _____

3. _____

Item Specific Feedback

Item Number	Feedback

Month-to-Month Guides
The Individualized Plan

The topics to be addressed in Months 4 through 6 were selected by you and your CS using the information from your self-reflection and self-assessment activities, as well as the assessments conducted by your CS. In month 6 you will re-do the New Supervisor Self-Assessment Foundational Supervision Skills and complete the New Supervisor Self-Assessment Advanced Supervision and Mentoring Skills to identify remaining content to address across Month 7 through Month 11 for yourself. You will simultaneously use your ongoing assessment of your trainees to continue to review and build their curricular roadmap and competencies. Planning is important but remember to be flexible. For your plan, you and your CS will use data from your self-assessments, joint evaluation of the effects of your consulting sessions, and any immediate needs to revisit, reorder, or add in new topics. You will do the same for your trainees' roadmaps. You may elect, for yourself or your trainees, to spend an additional month on a topic or move forward to a topic that has suddenly become pressing (e.g., crucial-conversations topic was scheduled for Month 8, but in Month 5 you realize you need to have one with your trainee now).

The following section provides outlines for Month 4 through 11 for you to plan your activities with your CS and your trainees, based on the drafted roadmaps and goals. Each month template contains a standard outline for you to enter specific topics and skills. You'll start by describing the specific skills and topics for the month for you and your trainees. For topics and skills that both you and your trainees need to work on, we recommend staggering them by one month so that you have an opportunity to discuss and practice with your CS and then prepare to address with your trainee. You will find a list of reminders for each month with prompts to complete specific activities, such as reassessing your own skills or your trainees' skills, complete your workload assessment, or solicit formal feedback from your trainees. Next, you will complete a section preparing for the monthly CS meeting and meetings and activities with your trainees. The next section should be completed after your meetings and observations, as it asks you to list follow-up actions and ideas for activities to do with your CoP. Finally, each month ends with the reflection activity.

Month 4
Selected Skills

Briefly describe the specific skills and topics to be covered this month from your roadmap and your trainees' roadmap.

Your Skills & Topics	Trainee Skills & Topics

Month 4 Reminders

- You will create and share the agenda for your Month 4 CS meeting (remember to include a standing item for signing the Consulting Supervision Documentation form).

- You will evaluate your trainees' agenda-related task.

- You will review your trainees' formal feedback, make plans to implement any needed changes, and discuss with your trainees.

- Complete the Month 4 Reflection activity at the end of the month.

- Check in on your own stress level and that of your trainees.

Preparation

Briefly describe the specific tasks you need to complete to prepare for your upcoming CS meetings and for your upcoming meetings and observations with your trainees. Remember to create and post the meeting agenda for your CS meeting and complete any activities related to agendas for meetings and observations with trainees (e.g., prepare observation agendas, prepare your sections of the meeting agenda as you hand over ownership, review the meeting agenda to provide feedback).

Preparation Tasks for CS Meeting	Preparation Tasks for Trainee Meetings & Observations

Follow-Up Action Items

Briefly list any actions or deliverables that were identified in your meetings and observations this month.

- _____
- _____
- _____
- _____

Ideas for CoP Activities

Briefly list any activities that you can engage in with your CoP based on the topics and skills covered in your CS meetings or with your trainees. Do your best to identify at least two things (e.g., specific discussion activity, reflection and share, and article to read and discuss, a resource to make and review).

1. _____

2. _____

Month 4 Reflection Activity

Topic/Task/Activity	What went well and how do you know?	What could use improvements and how do you know?	What will you do differently? Questions for your CS

Month 5
Selected Skills

Briefly describe the specific skills and topics to be covered this month from your roadmap and your trainees' roadmap.

Your Skills & Topics	Trainee Skills & Topics

Month 5 Reminders

- Complete the Month 5 Reflection activity at the end of the month.

- Check in on your own stress level and that of your trainees.

Preparation

Briefly describe the specific tasks you need to complete to prepare for your upcoming CS meetings and for your upcoming meetings and observations with your trainees. Remember to create and post the meeting agenda for your CS meeting and complete any activities related to agendas for meetings and observations with trainees (e.g., prepare observation agendas, prepare your sections of the meeting agenda as you hand over ownership, review the meeting agenda to provide feedback).

Preparation Tasks for CS Meeting	Preparation Tasks for Trainee Meetings & Observations

THE INDIVIDUALIZED PLAN

Follow-Up Action Items

Briefly list any actions or deliverables that were identified in your meetings and observations this month.

- _____

- _____

- _____

- _____

Ideas for CoP Activities

Briefly list any activities that you can engage in with your CoP based on the topics and skills covered in your CS meetings or with your trainees. Do your best to identify at least two things (e.g., specific discussion activity, reflection and share, and article to read and discuss, a resource to make and review).

1. _____

2. _____

Month 5 Reflection Activity

Topic/Task/ Activity	What went well and how do you know?	What could use improvements and how do you know?	What will you do differently? Questions for your CS

THE INDIVIDUALIZED PLAN

Month 6

Selected Skills

Briefly describe the specific skills and topics to be covered this month from your roadmap and your trainees' roadmap.

Your Skills & Topics	Trainee Skills & Topics

Month 6 Reminders

- Complete the Month 6 Workload Assessment *before* you meet with your CS. Plan to discuss with your CS how to incorporate using the Workload assessment with your trainees to facilitate conversations about time management, scope of competence, and work-life balance.

- Complete the New Supervisor Self-Assessment Foundational Supervision Skills re-assessment and compare to your initial assessment *before* you meet with your CS. You will note that the scoring is different than the first version you completed. That is because the scores for this version reflect the expectation that you may be reaching proficiency or fluency for some of these skills. Identify areas where you have improved, and areas for continued focus and growth.

- Complete the New Supervisor Self-Assessment Foundational Supervision Skills *before* you meet with your CS and identify preferred topics to add to your roadmap for Month 7 through Month 11.

- Complete continued skills and knowledge assessments of your trainees; add to their roadmap for Months 7 through 12 and be prepared to discuss with your CS.

- Have your trainees complete a formal-feedback activity to review with your CS.

- Complete the Month 6 Reflection activity at the end of the month.

- Check in on your own stress level and that of your trainees.

Preparation

Briefly describe the specific tasks you need to complete to prepare for your upcoming CS meetings and for your upcoming meetings and observations with your trainees. Remember to create and post the meeting agenda for your CS meeting and complete any activities related to agendas for meetings and observations with trainees (e.g., prepare observation agendas, prepare your sections of the meeting agenda as you hand over ownership, review the meeting agenda to provide feedback).

Preparation Tasks for CS Meeting	Preparation Tasks for Trainee Meetings & Observations

Follow-Up Action Items

Briefly list any actions or deliverables that were identified in your meetings and observations this month.

- _____
- _____
- _____
- _____

Ideas for CoP Activities

Briefly list any activities that you can engage in with your CoP based on the topics and skills covered in your CS meetings or with your trainees. Do your best to identify at least two things (e.g., specific discussion activity, reflection and share, and article to read and discuss, a resource to make and review).

1. _____
2. _____

Foundational Supervision Skills Self-Assessment

Re-Assessment in Month 6

Instructions: Rate each of the following supervision and mentorship skills as 3) proficient, 2) developing, 1) not yet acquired. Mark an asterisk (*) if your repertoire for this skill includes some problematic history and performance aspects (e.g., history of harsh feedback and you sometimes behave the same way when you give feedback).

- Score 3 for *proficient* if you perform the skill accurately and consistently with a little preparation, effort, and only minimal distractors..

- Score 2 for *developing* if you are not yet able to perform the skill consistently and accurately, even under optimal conditions.

- Score 1 for *not yet acquired* if you have not yet had the opportunity to learn the skill.

Specific Foundational Supervision Skills	Score
BACB Supervision Requirements	
1. Describe basic requirements (e.g., frequency of supervision, relevant activities, acceptable modalities, use of group supervision).	
2. Name and describe the purpose and how to use and access required documents and forms.	
3. Describe, create, use, and teach others how to use documentation systems.	
4. Develop a contract and review the contract with a supervisee or trainee using an informed-consent approach.	
TOTAL:	
Purpose of Supervision	
1. Describe the purpose for implementing behavior-analytic supervision (e.g., the benefits and desired outcomes).	
2. Describe the potential risks of ineffective supervision (e.g., poor client outcomes, poor supervisee performance).	
TOTAL:	

Specific Foundational Supervision Skills	Score
Structuring Supervision	
1. Develop a positive rapport.	
2. Schedule and run effective meetings based on LeBlanc & Nosik (2019) checklist.	
3. Establish clear performance expectations for the supervisor and supervisee or trainee.	
4. Conduct assessments of the supervisee or trainee.	
5. Select supervision goals based on an assessment to improve relevant skills (BACB Task List and Ethics Code related skills).	
TOTAL:	
Training and Performance Management	
1. Explain the purpose of feedback and discuss preferences for trainee to receive and give feedback.	
2. Use Behavior Skills Training (BST) in teaching supervisees and trainees.	
3. Train personnel to competently perform assessment and intervention procedures.	
4. Use performance monitoring, feedback, and reinforcement systems.	
5. Use a functional assessment approach (e.g., performance diagnostics) and tools (Performance Diagnostic Checklist-Human Services; PDC-HS) to identify variables affecting personnel performance.	
6. Use function-based strategies to improve personnel performance.	
TOTAL:	
Evaluating the Effects of Supervision	
1. Solicit, review, and respond to feedback from supervisees, trainees, and others.	
2. Evaluate the effects of supervision (e.g., on client outcomes, on supervisee repertoires).	
3. Implement changes when needed.	
TOTAL:	
Monitoring and Managing Stress and Wellness	
1. Monitor your own stress levels and detect the effects of stress on your supervisory skills and on others.	
2. Engage in appropriate self-care strategies to manage stress (i.e., identify alternative behaviors when you notice you are impacted by stress).	
3. Teach supervisees and trainees to monitor their stress levels and detect effects on others.	
4. Teach supervisees and trainees to engage in appropriate self-care strategies to manage stress.	
TOTAL:	

New Supervisor Self-Assessment Advanced Supervision and Mentoring Skills

Month 6

Instructions: Rate each of the following supervision and mentorship skills as 3) proficient, 2) developing, 1) not yet acquired. Mark an asterisk (*) if your repertoire for this skill includes some problematic history and performance aspects (e.g., history of harsh feedback and you sometimes behave the same way when you give feedback).

- Score 3 for *proficient* if you perform the skill accurately and consistently with little preparation, effort, and only minimal distractors.

- Score 2 for *developing* if you are not yet able to perform the skill consistently and accurately, even under optimal conditions.

- Score 1 for *not yet acquired* if you have not yet had the opportunity to learn the skill.

Specific Advanced Supervision Skills	Score
Maintaining Supervision	
1. Establish, and continually evaluate the health of bi-directional, collaborative supervisory relationships.	
2. Self-monitor your reactions to various supervisees and mentees to detect potential fractures in the supervisory relationship.	
3. Ask the supervisee open-ended questions to produce insight about their own actions, knowledge, and understanding.	
4. Identify and address cultural variables in supervisory relationships.	
5. Identify your own professional reinforcers to foster career sustainability.	
6. Assist your supervisees and trainees to identify their professional reinforcers to foster career sustainability.	
TOTAL:	

Specific Advanced Supervision Skills	Score

Training and Performance Management

1. Teach supervisees and trainees how to discuss and train feedback delivery and reception skills.
2. Prepare for and have crucial conversations with supervisees, families, colleagues, and supervisors.
3. Teach supervisees and trainees to prepare for and have crucial conversations with supervisees, families, colleagues, and supervisors.
4. Describe your own performance and the reasons why you performed that way while performing (i.e., a running, descriptive narrative while you are behaving).
5. Teach supervisees and trainees how to self-observe and describe their performance and the reasons for it while performing (i.e., how to use a running narrative to describe why they do what they do).
6. Teach supervisees and trainees to use Behavior Skills Training.
7. Guide supervisees and trainees through structured problem-solving analyses rather than solving problems for them.
8. Assess and address supervisees' and trainees' organization and time-management issues that impact professional performance.
9. Assess and address supervisees' and trainees' interpersonal-skill deficits that impact professional performance.

TOTAL:

Structuring Supervision

1. Teach supervisees and trainees to engage in self-evaluation.
2. Teach supervisees and trainees to solicit and evaluate feedback.
3. Teach supervisees and trainees to engage in self-monitoring.

TOTAL:

Monitoring and Managing Stress and Wellness

1. Create a structured self-monitoring plan to maintain self-care.
2. Access supports (e.g., colleagues, supervisors/mentors, professionals) to assist in problem-solving and managing stress.
3. Enhance and refine organization and time management (OTM) and problem-solving to decrease stress.
4. Teach supervisees and trainees to create a structured, self-monitoring plan to maintain self-care.
5. Teach supervisees and trainees to access supports (e.g., colleagues, supervisors/ mentors, professionals) to assist in problem-solving and managing stress.
6. Teach supervisees and trainees to enhance and refine OTM and problem-solving to decrease stress.

TOTAL:

Task	Average Weekly Time Requirement	Facilitators	Barriers
Client caseload management			
RBT caseload			
BCaBA caseload			
Trainee caseload			
Administrative responsibilities			
Other duties			
Total average weekly work hours:			

Month 6 Reflection Activity

Topic/Task/ Activity	What went well and how do you know?	What could use improvements and how do you know?	What will you do differently? Questions for your CS

THE INDIVIDUALIZED PLAN

Month 7
Selected Skills

Briefly describe the specific skills and topics to be covered this month from your roadmap and your trainees' roadmap.

Your Skills & Topics	Trainee Skills & Topics

Month 7 Reminders

- Review your trainees' formal feedback from Month 6 with your CS, make plans to implement any needed changes and discuss with your trainees.

- Complete the Month 7 Reflection activity at the end of the month.

- Check in on your own stress level and that of your trainees.

Preparation

Briefly describe the specific tasks you need to complete to prepare for your upcoming CS meetings and for your upcoming meetings and observations with your trainees. Remember to create and post the meeting agenda for your CS meeting and complete any activities related to agendas for meetings and observations with trainees (e.g., prepare observation agendas, prepare your sections of the meeting agenda as you hand over ownership, review the meeting agenda to provide feedback).

Preparation Tasks for CS Meeting	Preparation Tasks for Trainee Meetings & Observations

Follow-Up Action Items

Briefly list any actions or deliverables that were identified in your meetings and observations this month.

- _____
- _____
- _____
- _____

Ideas for CoP Activities

Briefly list any activities that you can engage in with your CoP based on the topics and skills covered in your CS meetings or with your trainees. Do your best to identify at least two things (e.g., specific discussion activity, reflection and share, and article to read and discuss, a resource to make and review).

1. _____
2. _____

THE INDIVIDUALIZED PLAN

Month 7 Reflection Activity

Topic/Task/ Activity	What went well and how do you know?	What could use improvements and how do you know?	What will you do differently? Questions for your CS

Month 8

Selected Skills

Briefly describe the specific skills and topics to be covered this month from your roadmap and your trainees' roadmap.

Your Skills & Topics	Trainee Skills & Topics

Month 8 Reminders

- Complete the Burnout Self-Assessment.

- Consider having your trainees complete it this month, or next month.

- Complete the Month 8 Reflection activity at the end of the month.

- Check in on your own stress level and that of your trainees.

Preparation

Briefly describe the specific tasks you need to complete to prepare for your upcoming CS meetings and for your upcoming meetings and observations with your trainees. Remember to create and post the meeting agenda for your CS meeting and complete any activities related to agendas for meetings and observations with trainees (e.g., prepare observation agendas, prepare your sections of the meeting agenda as you hand over ownership, review the meeting agenda to provide feedback).

Preparation Tasks for CS Meeting	Preparation Tasks for Trainee Meetings & Observations

Follow-Up Action Items

Briefly list any actions or deliverables that were identified in your meetings and observations this month.

- _____
- _____
- _____
- _____

Ideas for CoP Activities

Briefly list any activities that you can engage in with your CoP based on the topics and skills covered in your CS meetings or with your trainees. Do your best to identify at least two things (e.g., specific discussion activity, reflection and share, and article to read and discuss, a resource to make and review).

1. _____

2. _____

🧠 Month 8 Reflection Activity

Topic/Task/ Activity	What went well and how do you know?	What could use improvements and how do you know?	What will you do differently? Questions for your CS

THE INDIVIDUALIZED PLAN

Month 8 Burnout Self-Assessment

The Copenhagen Burnout Inventory (CPI)   Kristensen et al. (2005)

Instructions: Review the definitions of the three categories below, then score each question by entering the score value (e.g., 100, 75, 50, 25, 0) in the scoring column.

From Kristensen et al. (p. 197, 2005):

> *"Personal burnout is the degree of physical and psychological fatigue and exhaustion experienced by the person."*

> *Client-related burnout: "The degree of physical and psychological fatigue and exhaustion that is perceived by the person as related to his/her work with clients."*

> *Work-related burnout: "The degree of physical and psychological fatigue and exhaustion that is perceived by the person as related to his/her work."*

Items	Always or to a very high degree (100)	Often or to a high degree (75)	Sometimes or somewhat (50)	Seldom or to a low degree (25)	Never or almost never; to a very low degree (0)
Personal Burnout					
How often do you feel tired?					
How often are you physically exhausted?					
How often are you emotionally exhausted?					
How often do you think, "I can't take it anymore"?					
How often do you feel worn out?					
How often do you feel weak and susceptible to illness?					
Scoring Category Totals:					
Personal Burnout Total:					

Items	Always or to a very high degree (100)	Often or to a high degree (75)	Sometimes or somewhat (50)	Seldom or to a low degree (25)	Never or almost never; to a very low degree (0)
Work-Related Burnout					
Do you feel worn out at the end of the working day?					
Are you exhausted in the morning at the thought of another day at work?					
Do you feel that every working hour is tiring for you?					
Do you have enough energy for family and friends during leisure time?					
Is your work emotionally exhausting?					
Does your work frustrate you?					
Do you feel burnt out because of your work?					
Scoring Category Totals:					
Work-Related Burnout Total:					
Client-Related Burnout					
Do you find it hard to work with clients?					
Does it drain your energy to work with clients?					
Do you find it frustrating to work with clients?					
Do you feel that you give more than you get back when you work with clients?					
Are you tired of working with clients?					
Do you sometimes wonder how long you will be able to continue working with clients?					
Scoring Category Totals:					
Client-Related Burnout Total:					

FINAL SCORE: _____

The higher the total score, the greater the degree of burnout. Review the total scores for each category to identify if the level of burnout is consistent across all three or if it is higher in one of the categories. Work to identify strategies to address the effects of burnout for yourself or your trainees in the workplace and your personal lives. A number of journal articles are published by behavior analysts that outline and describe strategies to engage in active self-care and self-compassion practices to work toward achieving a healthy work-life balance and a sustained career. Many of the articles include descriptions of specific activities and practices, as well as robust resources (e.g., self-care assessments, recommended actions, books, web applications) to support you in your endeavors. Here are a few to get you started.

Self-Care and Burnout Specific Articles

Coyne, L. W., Gould, E. R., Grimaldi, M., Wilson, K. G., Baffuto, G., & Biglan, A. (2021). First things first: Parent psychological flexibility and self-compassion during COVID-19. *Behavior Analysis in Practice, 14*(4), 1092-1098.

Fiebig, J. H., Gould, E. R., Ming, S., & Watson, R. A. (2020). An invitation to act on the value of self-care: Being a whole person in all that you do. *Behavior Analysis in Practice*, 1-9.

Slowiak, J. M., & De Longchamp, A. C. (2021). Self-care strategies and job-crafting practices among behavior analysts: Do they predict perceptions of work–life balance, work engagement, and burnout? *Behavior Analysis in Practice*, 1-19.

Month 9

Selected Skills

Briefly describe the specific skills and topics to be covered this month from your roadmap and your trainees' roadmap.

Your Skills & Topics	Trainee Skills & Topics

Month 9 Reminders

- Complete the Month 9 Workload Assessment *before* you meet with your CS.

- Have your trainees complete a formal-feedback activity.

- Complete the Month 9 Reflection activity at the end of the month.

- Check in on your own stress level and that of your trainees.

Preparation

Briefly describe the specific tasks you need to complete to prepare for your upcoming CS meetings and for your upcoming meetings and observations with your trainees. Remember to create and post the meeting agenda for your CS meeting and complete any activities related to agendas for meetings and observations with trainees (e.g., prepare observation agendas, prepare your sections of the meeting agenda as you hand over ownership, review the meeting agenda to provide feedback).

Preparation Tasks for CS Meeting	Preparation Tasks for Trainee Meetings & Observations

Follow-Up Action Items

Briefly list any actions or deliverables that were identified in your meetings and observations this month.

- _____
- _____
- _____
- _____

Ideas for CoP Activities

Briefly list any activities that you can engage in with your CoP based on the topics and skills covered in your CS meetings or with your trainees. Do your best to identify at least two things (e.g., specific discussion activity, reflection and share, and article to read and discuss, a resource to make and review).

1. _____

2. _____

Task	Average Weekly Time Requirement	Facilitators	Barriers
Client caseload management			
RBT caseload			
BCaBA caseload			
Trainee caseload			
Administrative responsibilities			
Other duties			
Total average weekly work hours:			

Month 9 Reflection Activity

Topic/Task/ Activity	What went well and how do you know?	What could use improvements and how do you know?	What will you do differently? Questions for your CS

Month 10
Selected Skills

Briefly describe the specific skills and topics to be covered this month from your roadmap and your trainees' roadmap.

Your Skills & Topics	Trainee Skills & Topics

Month 10 Reminders

- You will review your trainees' formal feedback from Month 9, make plans to implement any needed changes and discuss with your trainees.

- Complete the Month 10 Reflection activity at end of the month.

- Check in on your own stress level and that of your trainees.

- You are in the home stretch, but there are several activities to complete in preparation for Month 12. Consider starting to review them now so you can calendar time toward the end of this month and throughout Month 11.

THE INDIVIDUALIZED PLAN

Preparation

Briefly describe the specific tasks you need to complete to prepare for your upcoming CS meetings and for your upcoming meetings and observations with your trainees. Remember to create and post the meeting agenda for your CS meeting and complete any activities related to agendas for meetings and observations with trainees (e.g., prepare observation agendas, prepare your sections of the meeting agenda as you hand over ownership, review the meeting agenda to provide feedback).

Preparation Tasks for CS Meeting	Preparation Tasks for Trainee Meetings & Observations

Follow-Up Action Items

Briefly list any actions or deliverables that were identified in your meetings and observations this month.

- _____

- _____

- _____

- _____

Ideas for CoP Activities

Briefly list any activities that you can engage in with your CoP based on the topics and skills covered in your CS meetings or with your trainees. Do your best to identify at least two things (e.g., specific discussion activity, reflection and share, and article to read and discuss, a resource to make and review).

1. _____

2. _____

Month 10 Reflection Activity

Topic/Task/ Activity	What went well and how do you know?	What could use improvements and how do you know?	What will you do differently? Questions for your CS

THE INDIVIDUALIZED PLAN

Month 11

Selected Skills

Briefly describe the specific skills and topics to be covered this month from your roadmap and your trainees' roadmap.

Your Skills & Topics	Trainee Skills & Topics

Month 11 Reminders

- Complete the Month 11 Reflection activity at the end of the month.

- Check in on your own stress level and that of your trainees.

- Continue reviewing and working on Month 12 Preparation Activities.

Preparation

Briefly describe the specific tasks you need to complete to prepare for your upcoming CS meetings and for your upcoming meetings and observations with your trainees. Remember to create and post the meeting agenda for your CS meeting and complete any activities related to agendas for meetings and observations with trainees (e.g., prepare observation agendas, prepare your sections of the meeting agenda as you hand over ownership, review the meeting agenda to provide feedback).

Preparation Tasks for CS Meeting	Preparation Tasks for Trainee Meetings & Observations

Follow-Up Action Items

Briefly list any actions or deliverables that were identified in your meetings and observations this month.

- _____
- _____
- _____
- _____

Ideas for CoP Activities

Briefly list any activities that you can engage in with your CoP based on the topics and skills covered in your CS meetings or with your trainees. Do your best to identify at least two things (e.g., specific discussion activity, reflection and share, and article to read and discuss, a resource to make and review).

1. _____
2. _____

THE INDIVIDUALIZED PLAN

Month 11 Reflection Activity

Topic/Task/ Activity	What went well and how do you know?	What could use improvements and how do you know?	What will you do differently? Questions for your CS

Month 12
Facilitating Effective Professional-Development Planning

WOW! You made it!

Take a few deep breaths, drop your shoulders away from your ears, and take a pause to appreciate this moment. You now have eleven full months of supported supervision under your belt. Because you took a planful approach and, yes, put in extra effort, these past months have provided you with valuable experiences and lessons to establish strong supervisory repertoires to maximize the positive impact you will have on trainees and clients now and forever. This last month with your CS is all about reflecting and planning for your own career sustainability and planning for the remaining time you have with your current trainees.

Goals for upcoming CS meeting

- Review your own progress over the past 11 months.
- Plan for your continued professional development.
- Review trainees' progress over the past 11 months (evaluating effects of your supervision).
- Review roadmap for trainees' remaining months.
- Express gratitude.

Goals for upcoming trainee meetings

- Review trainees' progress over the past 11 months and effects of your supervision.
- Have an open feedback conversation.
- Review the roadmap for trainees' remaining months.
- Express gratitude.

Complete the following tasks in preparation of your last meeting with your CS.

PREP TASK 1 – Revisit Values Activity: Complete the Values Identification Activity (below). Once you are done, go back to the values-related activities you completed in previous months (i.e., the values-related question from the Self-Reflection activity in the Getting Ready section, the Values Identification Activity you first completed in Month 1, and the Month 2 Self-Reflection on Culturally Responsive and Humble Practices) and compare your answers. Please wait to review your past response until *after* you have completed the activity below, as we do not want your current responses to be informed by your past ones. While reviewing your current and past responses consider the following questions: 1) Have my responses changed? 2) If so, in what ways and in which areas? Be prepared to review and discuss with your CS.

Notes: _____

_____

_____

Values Identification Activity

Domain	Value	Example of Behaving Consistently with this Value	Strategy for Conveying this Value to Your Trainee
Practice			
Supervision			

PREP TASK 2 – Complete Burnout Assessment: Complete the Burnout Self-Evaluation (on the following page). Once you are done, go back to the one you completed in Month 8 and compare your score and answers. As with the last prep activity, please wait to review your past response until *after* you have completed the activity on the following page, as we do not want your current responses to be informed by your past ones. While reviewing your current and past responses consider the following questions: 1) Have my responses changed? 2) If so, in what ways and in which areas? Be prepared to review and discuss with your CS.

Notes: _____

_____

_____

The Copenhagen Burnout Inventory (CPI) Kristensen et al. (2005)

Instructions: Review the definitions of the three categories below, then score each question by entering the score value (e.g., 100, 75, 50, 25, 0) in the scoring column.

From Kristensen et al. (p. 197, 2005):

> *"Personal burnout is the degree of physical and psychological fatigue and exhaustion experienced by the person."*

> *Client-related burnout: "The degree of physical and psychological fatigue and exhaustion that is perceived by the person as related to his/her work with clients."*

> *Work-related burnout: "The degree of physical and psychological fatigue and exhaustion that is perceived by the person as related to his/her work."*

Items	Always or to a very high degree (100)	Often or to a high degree (75)	Sometimes or somewhat (50)	Seldom or to a low degree (25)	Never or almost never; to a very low degree (0)
Personal Burnout					
How often do you feel tired?					
How often are you physically exhausted?					
How often are you emotionally exhausted?					
How often do you think, "I can't take it anymore"?					
How often do you feel worn out?					
How often do you feel weak and susceptible to illness?					
Scoring Category Totals:					
Personal Burnout Total:					
Work-Related Burnout					
Do you feel worn out at the end of the working day?					
Are you exhausted in the morning at the thought of another day at work?					
Do you feel that every working hour is tiring for you?					
Do you have enough energy for family and friends during leisure time?					
Is your work emotionally exhausting?					
Does your work frustrate you?					
Do you feel burnt out because of your work?					
Scoring Category Totals:					
Work-Related Burnout Total:					

Items	Always or to a very high degree (100)	Often or to a high degree (75)	Sometimes or somewhat (50)	Seldom or to a low degree (25)	Never or almost never; to a very low degree (0)
Client-Related Burnout					
Do you find it hard to work with clients?					
Does it drain your energy to work with clients?					
Do you find it frustrating to work with clients?					
Do you feel that you give more than you get back when you work with clients?					
Are you tired of working with clients?					
Do you sometimes wonder how long you will be able to continue working with clients?					
Scoring Category Totals:					
Client-Related Burnout Total:					

FINAL SCORE: _____

PREP TASK 3 – Complete Wrap-Up Reflection Activity: Spend some time reflecting on the past eleven months with your CS and your trainees and answer the questions below.

1. What are the two most helpful things that your CS has done with you?

2. What are two things you think your CS could do better with other NSs?

3. What was the hardest lesson you learned?

4. What was the easiest lesson you learned?

5. In what ways have your perceptions about the value of high-quality supervision changed?

6. What are two things you have learned from your trainees?

7. What are two things you will do differently with future trainees?

PREP TASK 4 – Complete Workload Assessment: Complete your Workload Assessment, compare with past results, and prepare to discuss with your CS.

Workload Assessment Month 12

Task	Average Weekly Time Requirement	Facilitators	Barriers
Client caseload management			
RBT caseload			
BCaBA caseload			
Trainee caseload			
Administrative responsibilities			
Other duties			
Total average weekly work hours:			

Notes: _____

_____

_____

PREP TASK 5 – Complete a Re-assessment of the New Supervisor Self-Assessment Foundational Supervision Skills and New Supervisor Self-Assessment Advanced Supervision and Mentoring Skills assessments: Fill out the two self-assessments and then compare your past results. You will use the results for the next prep task. Share the results with your CS *before* your Month 12 meeting.

New Supervisor Self-Assessment Foundational Supervision Skills

Month 12 Re-Assessment

Instructions: Rate each of the following supervision and mentorship skills as 3) proficient, 2) developing, 1) not yet acquired. Mark an asterisk (*) if your repertoire for this skill includes some problematic history and performance aspects (e.g., history of harsh feedback and you sometimes behave the same way when you give feedback).

- Score 3 for *proficient* if you perform the skill accurately and consistently with a little preparation, effort, and only minimal distractors..

- Score 2 for *developing* if you are not yet able to perform the skill consistently and accurately, even under optimal conditions.

- Score 1 for *not yet acquired* if you have not yet had the opportunity to learn the skill.

Specific Foundational Supervision Skill	Score
BACB Supervision Requirements	
1. Describe basic requirements (e.g., frequency of supervision, relevant activities, acceptable modalities, use of group supervision).	
2. Name, describe the purpose and how to use, and access required documents and forms.	
3. Describe, create, use, and teach others how to use documentation systems.	
4. Develop a contract and review the contract with a supervisee or trainee using an informed-consent approach.	
TOTAL:	
Purpose of Supervision	
1. Describe the purpose for implementing behavior-analytic supervision (e.g., the benefits and desired outcomes).	
2. Describe the potential risks of ineffective supervision (e.g., poor client outcomes, poor supervisee performance).	
TOTAL:	
Structuring Supervision	
1. Develop a positive rapport.	
2. Schedule and run effective meetings based on the LeBlanc & Nosik (2019) checklist.	

Specific Foundational Supervision Skill	Score
3. Establish clear performance expectations for the supervisor and supervisee or trainee.	
4. Conduct assessments of the supervisee or trainee.	
5. Select supervision goals based on an assessment to improve relevant skills (BACB Task List and Ethics Code related skills).	
TOTAL:	

Training and Performance Management

	Score
1. Explain the purpose of feedback and discuss preferences for the trainee to receive and give feedback.	
2. Use Behavior Skills Training (BST) in teaching supervisees and trainees.	
3. Train personnel to competently perform assessment and intervention procedures.	
4. Use performance monitoring, feedback, and reinforcement systems.	
5. Use a functional-assessment approach (e.g., performance diagnostics) and tools (Performance Diagnostic Checklist-Human Services; PDC-HS) to identify variables affecting personnel performance.	
6. Use function-based strategies to improve personnel performance.	
TOTAL:	

Evaluating the Effects of Supervision

	Score
1. Solicit, review, and respond to feedback from supervises, trainees, and others.	
2. Evaluate the effects of supervision (e.g., on client outcomes, on supervisee repertoires).	
3. Implement changes when needed.	
TOTAL:	

Monitoring and Managing Stress and Wellness

	Score
1. Monitor your own stress levels and detect the effects of stress on your supervisory skills and on others.	
2. Engage in appropriate self-care strategies to manage stress (i.e., identify alternative behaviors when you notice you are impacted by stress).	
3. Teach supervisees and trainees to monitor their stress levels and detect effects on others.	
4. Teach supervisees and trainees to engage in appropriate self-care strategies to manage stress.	
TOTAL:	

New Supervisor Self-Assessment Advanced Supervision and Mentoring Skills

Month 12 Re-Assessment

Instructions: Rate each of the following supervision and mentorship skills as 3) proficient, 2) developing, 1) not yet acquired. Mark an asterisk (*) if your repertoire for this skill includes some problematic history and performance aspects (e.g., history of harsh feedback and you sometimes behave the same way when you give feedback).

- Score 3 for *proficient* if you perform the skill accurately and consistently with a little preparation, effort, and only minimal distractors..
- Score 2 for *developing* if you are not yet able to perform the skill consistently and accurately, even under optimal conditions.
- Score 1 for *not yet acquired* if you have not yet had the opportunity to learn the skill.

Specific Advanced Supervision Skill	Score
Maintaining Supervision	
1. Establish, and continually evaluate the health of bi-directional, collaborative supervisory relationships.	
2. Self-monitor your reactions to various supervisees and mentees to detect potential fractures in the supervisory relationship.	
3. Ask the supervisees open-ended questions to produce insight about their own actions, knowledge, and understanding.	
4. Identify and address cultural variables in supervisory relationships.	
5. Identify your own professional reinforcers to foster career sustainability.	
6. Assist your supervisees and trainees to identify their professional reinforcers to foster career sustainability.	
TOTAL:	

Specific Advanced Supervision Skill	Score
Training and Performance Management	
1. Teach supervisees and trainees how to discuss and train feedback delivery and reception skills.	
2. Prepare for and have crucial conversations with supervisees, families, colleagues, and supervisors.	
3. Teach supervisees and trainees to prepare for and have crucial conversations with supervisees, families, colleagues, and supervisors.	
4. Describe your own performance and the reasons why you performed that way while performing (i.e., a running, descriptive narrative while you are behaving).	
5. Teach supervisees and trainees how to self-observe and describe their performance and the reasons for it while performing (i.e., how to use a running narrative to describe why they do what they do).	
6. Teach supervisees and trainees to use Behavior Skills Training.	
7. Guide supervisees and trainees through structured problem-solving analyses rather than solving problems for them.	
8. Assess and address supervisee and trainees' organization and time-management issues that impact professional performance.	
9. Assess and address supervisees' and trainees' interpersonal skill deficits that impact professional performance.	
TOTAL:	
Evaluating the Effects of Supervision	
1. Teach supervisees and trainees to engage in self-evaluation.	
2. Teach supervisees and trainees to solicit and evaluate feedback.	
3. Teach supervisees and trainees to engage in self-monitoring.	
TOTAL:	
Monitoring and Managing Stress and Wellness	
1. Create a structured self-monitoring plan to maintain self-care.	
2. Access supports (e.g., colleagues, supervisors/mentors, professionals) to assist in problem-solving and managing stress.	
3. Enhance and refine organization and time management (OTM) and problem-solving to decrease stress.	
4. Teach supervisees and trainees to create a structured self-monitoring plan to maintain self-care.	
5. Teach supervisees and trainees to access supports (e.g., colleagues, supervisors/ mentors, professionals) to assist in problem-solving and managing stress.	
6. Teach supervisees and trainees to enhance and refine OTM and problem-solving to decrease stress.	
TOTAL:	

PREP TASK 4 – Draft Goals for Continued Professional Development: Using the results of your past and current self-assessments, draft some goals for your continued professional development. Remember that you need continuing education (CE) credits to maintain your BACB certification, so use them wisely by planning on how you will allocate numbers of credits to different important topics such as the following: requirements; areas to maintain, improve, expand; areas to explore; and areas for personal interest. Four important goals to consider and discuss with your CS are 1) maintaining your passion for high-quality supervision, 2) sustaining (or creating) a functioning CoP, 3) developing a relationship with at least one strong mentor, and 4) cultivating your wellness plan and activities. Share your draft goals with your CS *before* your Month 12 meeting.

Notes: _____

_____

_____

PREP TASK 5 – Review Trainees' Roadmaps: Review your trainees' roadmaps and any ongoing skills and knowledge assessments that you have been completing. Think about the remaining skills and begin to map them out for the remaining months you have in your supervision relationship with your trainees. Plan to share your draft with your CS.

Notes: _____

_____

_____

Checklist for Preparing for CS Month 12 Meeting

☐ Values Identification Activity.

☐ Burnout Assessment.

☐ Wrap-Up Reflection Activity.

☐ Workload Assessment.

☐ Re-Assess Foundational and Advanced Supervision Skills.

☐ Draft Continued Professional Development Goals.

☐ Review Trainee's Roadmaps and Draft Plan for Remaining Months.

During your last meeting with your CS, you will focus on looking back to review and forward to plan for yourself and for your current trainees.

1. Review Trainee Meetings and Observations: Keep this brief, as you will have a specific task to review their progress and your drafted plan to keep them moving forward.

   Notes: _____

   _____

   _____

2. Values Identification and Burnout Check-In: Review the results of your values and burnout assessments and reflection. If you have specific questions or ideas for actions you'd like to take, share them with your CS.

   Notes: _____

   _____

   _____

3. Wrap-Up Reflection Review: Spend a few minutes sharing some of the highlights from your reflection.

   Notes: _____

   _____

   _____

4. Planning for Your Continued Professional Development: Use the information from your workload assessment, skills assessment, and draft goals activities to discuss mapping out the tasks and activities for you to ensure continued professional development. Your CS will provide additional ideas and guidance to inform your drafted goals and plan.

   Notes: _____

   _____

   _____

5. Planning Remaining Month in Trainees' Roadmaps: Review your draft plans for the content to cover in the remaining months you have with your trainees and discuss with your CS.

   Notes: _____

   _____

   _____

6. Wrap-Up: Spend a few minutes thanking your CS for their time and effort over the past year. Review any follow-up tasks that you have.

After Month 12 Meeting with Your CS

Review and complete the following activities:

- Make needed revisions to your plan for continued professional development.
- Make needed revisions to your trainees' roadmaps.
- Gather any resources that your CS directed you to for your professional development and your trainees' roadmap.
- Send your CS a thank-you card or email.

Month 12 Trainee Meetings and Observation Activities

Before Month 12 Meetings with Your Trainee

Complete the following tasks in preparation of your upcoming meetings and observations with your trainees. Remember that these activities should be spread across several meetings and observations, as the BACB requires multiple contacts each month. It is up to you to split these activities across your trainee meetings as appropriate for the time schedule and the needs present in each meeting.

PREP TASK 1 – Prepare Meeting and Observation Agendas: Make agendas for upcoming meetings and observations and review any portions that you have turned over to your trainees. Include time to check in and review how things went in the past month.

PREP TASK 2 – Review Meeting and Observation Notes: Look back over the notes from your meetings, observations, and product reviews (if relevant) to prepare for the upcoming meeting.

PREP TASK 3 – Prepare to Discuss Feedback: Review all the formal-feedback forms that your trainees have completed, as well as other related notes that you have jotted down in your reflection activities. Be prepared to facilitate an open discussion about your supervisory practices, the feedback that you have been given, and changes that you have made. If possible, facilitate a conversation about what trainees think is going well and what you can do more of/less of. Try asking questions such as the following:

- What is one thing I can do right away that will help you be more successful?
- What is one thing I can stop doing immediately that will help you be more successful?
- What is something we could try together to facilitate our learning?
- I know it might be a bit uncomfortable to share your feedback directly with me. I value your thoughts *very* much. Do you think you could try helping be become a better supervisor by sharing one thing I can work on to better support you and my other trainees?

If your trainees are reluctant to provide you with direct, specific feedback in your meeting, that is okay; don't push. Let them know that you will send them another feedback form after the meeting.

PREP TASK 4 – Planning Remaining Curricular Roadmap: Review trainees' results of assessments and roadmaps and the notes from your last CS meeting. Prepare the draft plan for the remaining months with your trainees and draft some questions to facilitate feedback and ideas from your trainees.

Checklist for Preparing for Trainee Month 12 Meetings

☐ Prep/review agendas for Month 12 meetings and observations.

☐ Review past meeting and observation notes.

☐ Prepare feedback discussion.

☐ Prepare curricular roadmap content for remaining months.

During Month 12 Meetings with Your Trainee

1. **Check In:** Check in with your trainee to gauge stress levels and current needs.

2. **Review Last Meeting:** Review any follow-up tasks that were assigned from the last meetings.

3. **Review Observations and Products**

4. **Client-Related Tasks**

5. **BACB Task List/Behavior Analytic Topics/Tasks**

6. **Feedback Discussion:** Frame the discussion as a protected opportunity to review and reflect on the effects of your supervisory practice and feedback you have received. Communicate how much you value the feedback your trainees have provided to you. One way to do this is to share one or two specific examples of things that you have changed based on their feedback (or even just on your observations of and reflections on interactions and activities). Invite your trainee to provide you with direct feedback in the meeting by asking open-ended questions (see the examples from the related prep task).

7. **Complete Roadmap:** Review the drafted plan for the remaining months that you have with your trainees. Highlight topics and skills mastered and those with significant progress. Review the remaining topics and skills and describe why each is important to successful, independent practice as a clinician. Ask for the feedback and ideas from your trainee about the order of the remaining content and activities or opportunities they would find meaningful. If possible, revise the roadmap document in the meeting. Let them know that you will continue to review and revise it after the meeting and send a copy within two days.

8. **Wrap-Up:** Wrap up the meeting by expressing gratitude for the hard work your trainee has put into the past months. Consider sharing a brief summary of the one or two most important things you have learned from your time with your CS and your time with your trainee. Always make sure to sign any required forms!

After Month 12 Meetings with Your Trainee

Carry out any follow-up tasks from the meeting with your trainee and plan for other meetings and observations that will take place with your trainee during the month.

- Review and send the updated curricular roadmap.

- Send any deliverables identified from the meeting (e.g., formal-feedback form, articles).

- Complete Month 12 Trainee Reflection activity.

Month 12 Reflection Activity

Topic/Task/ Activity	What went well and how do you know?	What could use improvements and how do you know?	What will you do differently? Questions for your CS

👥 Month 12 Activities for PEERS/CoP

- Review your reflection activities with each other. Are there common themes?

- Review your plans for continued development with each other? Are there common goals? Are there opportunities to work collaboratively on addressing goals? Are there resources to share?

- Review the discussions you had with trainees on feedback and if any strategies for soliciting direct feedback were successful.

- Review your trainees' curricular roadmaps. Discuss topics such as how often you have had to modify them over the past months, how you solicited ideas from trainees, how you were able to incorporate those ideas. Review the remaining content and identify opportunities to share the burden for developing competencies and related materials and resources.

- Outline a plan to continue to meet regularly and goals for those meetings.

All right, we again say CONGRATULATIONS!!!!

What a journey you have been on! We hope that this workbook, and the companion workbook your CS may have been using, has been helpful in putting some structure to your first year of supervisory practice. We hope that the material highlighted how critical high-quality supervision is, and how the repertoires needed to be successful go way beyond the BACB Task List and behavior-analytic knowledge and skills. We are quite sure that you are just as busy as ever right now, but we invite you to set aside some time and reflect on the gift that you have given to your trainees, clients, CS, and the profession over this past year. We are confident that, although tired, you are well positioned to continue to give that effort time and again for the remainder of your career. Thank you, from the bottom of our hearts, for the work you do to make this world a better place.

Specific Skills

This section includes skills selected by you and your CS and added to your Yearly Planning Guide/Roadmap for Months 4-11. You should also select skills from this section to add into your trainees' roadmaps and use throughout the supervisory relationship. The skills included in this section do not represent an exhaustive list of the skills necessary to be a successful independent supervisor. Instead, we selected eleven specific skills that we consider foundational for you as a new supervisor, and for your supervisees and trainees who will soon become supervisors. These are skills that go above and beyond the BACB® Task List and the content included in the Getting Ready and the Early Months sections. These skills are critical to success, career longevity, and developing more-advanced skills. The eleven skills are listed in alphabetical order below:

1. **Compassionate Care and Therapeutic Relationships**
2. **Enhancing Learning: Self-Monitoring, Describing, and Asking Meaningful Questions**
3. **Evaluating Effects of Supervision**
4. **Feedback and Difficult Conversations**
5. **Ongoing Monitoring and Performance Management**
6. **Organization and Time Management**
7. **Problem-Solving and Decision Making**
8. **Public Speaking and Professional Presentations**
9. **Scope of Competence**
10. **Self-Care**
11. **Teaching BST and Training Strategies**

Each section includes information that will be most relevant to developing your skills and information that applies to developing the related skills of supervisees and trainees. You and your CS should use the information from your skills assessments, as well as naturally arising needs, to select the most relevant skills from this section to include in your roadmap for Month 4 through Month 11. However, we recognize the complexities of supervisory practice, and acknowledge that extra time may be spent working on one skill to mastery. Therefore, we include strategies and resources that you can use should you need to address some of the skills development on your own after the relationship with your CS has ended.

Each specific skill includes the following sections:

1. a brief description of the skill(s),
2. a brief description of why the skill(s) is(are) important,
3. strategies for how to assess the skill(s),
4. suggestions for how to teach the skill(s), and
5. additional resources.

In the assessment section, specific strategies for assessing the skills are described and a table is provided with indicators for you and for your supervisees/trainees to assist in evaluating if a skill is not yet acquired or is developing. Knowing where an individual is along the scope of skill development can help best identify teaching strategies and opportunities for shaping the skill. The teaching section discusses strategies for developing the relevant skill and includes a table with several possible, reflective practices and actions. The strategies can be used collaboratively with you and your CS to build your skills. Set goals for yourself, track progress, add the skill to your monthly agenda, and share how things are going with your CS. If you are struggling with a particular skill, be sure to allot an appropriate amount of time on the agenda to discuss. Spend time before the meeting reflecting, gathering data, and preparing specific questions. In the meeting, if needed, ask for the opportunity to role-play or practice with your CS. You can also use the strategies to build the skills of your supervisees or trainees, adding content to their competency-based roadmap, agendas, and observation checklists as needed. Finally, you can use the reflective strategies and actions to continue to build your skills in the months following the completion of your first year and throughout your supervisory career, revisiting when relevant.

Compassionate Care and Therapeutic Relationships

What These Are

Taylor et al. (2019) described *compassionate care* as providing services with an emphasis on empathy, compassion, and collaboration. Empathy involves both perceiving the feelings of others and understanding those emotions based on your own prior experiences with similar emotions. Compassion care involves acting based on your understanding of the other person's experience in an effort to support them and alleviate their suffering.

Compassionate care occurs in the context of a therapeutic relationship with the client and family. Therapeutic relationships are enhanced when behavior analysts practice skills in the domain of listening and collaboration, demonstrate empathy and compassion, and avoid various "negative" behaviors that could contribute to problems in the therapeutic relationship (Taylor et al., 2019). See Taylor et al. (2019) for a full list of these skills, behaviors to avoid, and a proposed curriculum of skills to teach.

Why They Are Important

Taylor et al. (2019) made the case that therapeutic relationship skills (e.g., empathy, compassion, rapport building) are a critical part of the repertoire of a successful BCBA because of the potential positive impact on family satisfaction, adherence to treatment, and improved clinical outcomes. Taylor et al. further hypothesized that failure to engage in critical relationship skills may negatively impact treatment, including parental nonsupport of treatment recommendations,

requests for reassignment to a different clinician, or termination of behavior-analytic services altogether. Use of these therapeutic relationship skills to create effective working relationships with clients and families can also directly influence practitioners themselves. LeBlanc, Sellers et al. (2020) describe that lack of these skills can lead to conflict-laden relationships with families which can erode professional experiences and lead to burnout for behavior analysts. Unfortunately, most behavior analysts are not trained in these skills as a part of their graduate training (LeBlanc et al., 2019). Whereas those articles were specific to the importance of compassionate care in the context of the therapeutic relationship between a clinician and a caregiver or client, it makes sense that many of the considerations and skills are also relevant to the supervisory relationship. In fact, LeBlanc, Sellers et al. (2020) describe these skills as a pivotal professional repertoire that should be explicitly taught in supervision.

Assessing These Skills

A supervisor could use a variety of strategies for assessing these skills. First, the supervisor could ask a supervisee or trainee to self-assess their use of specific strategies to establish and nurture a healthy therapeutic relationship with caregivers, supervisees, and trainees. LeBlanc, Sellers et al. (2020) provide a checklist for this purpose in Chapter 8. Second, these skills could be assessed and taught during role-plays of interactions with parents, supervisees, or trainees. The fifth column of Table 5 in Taylor et al. (2019) provides a list of suggested measures that could be used during performance assessments. Third, these skills can be assessed by observing interactions with clients and families or supervisees and trainees to identify the presence or absence of component skills and by seeking feedback about those skills from clients, families, supervisees, and trainees via surveys. The basic skill indicators are described here.

Skill Level	New BCBA	Supervisees/Trainees
Not yet acquired	✓ Never or infrequently makes reflective statements during active listening. ✓ Never or infrequently detects when a caregiver, client, supervisee, or trainee is becoming distressed. ✓ Always or frequently pushes their own agenda or does not acknowledge the ideas, priorities or concerns of client, caregiver, supervisee, or trainee. ✓ Unable to fluently describe what it might feel like to experience the daily concerns of the client, caregivers, supervisee, or trainee (i.e., perspective taking). ✓ Infrequently or never alters interactions in response to indicators that the other person is upset, agitated, or withdrawing. ✓ Is not able to tolerate the discomfort that occurs when a caregiver, client, supervisee, or trainee engages in emotional responding (e.g., crying, expressing sadness).	✓ Same
Developing	✓ Makes some reflective statements during active listening. ✓ Detects at least some instances of distress even if they are not the earliest indicators. ✓ Frequently acknowledges the ideas, priorities and concerns of the caregiver, client, supervisee, or trainee and collaboratively designs programming based on these. ✓ Able to engage in perspective-taking with respect to the experience of others (e.g., caring for a child with special needs, trying new and difficult skills). ✓ Demonstrates some responsiveness to indicators that the other person is upset, agitated, or withdrawing (e.g., sitting quietly to actively listen and responding empathetically when a caregiver, supervisee, or trainee is distressed or crying).	✓ Same

Teaching These Skills

A supervisor could use a variety of strategies to teach these skills. First, the supervisor could engage in an array of perspective-taking exercises with the supervisee or trainee. The supervisor could present a description of someone's circumstances along with a partial list of values (e.g., wanting to be a good parent and protect their child), concerns (e.g., will my child ever be able to live independently?), and priorities (e.g., teach them to talk) that they might have. They can then ask the supervisee or trainee to describe what it might feel like to live in these circumstances, providing descriptions if the supervisee cannot do so. The supervisor can also ask the supervisee or trainee to generate additional values, worries, priorities, or biases that the person in those circumstances might have. Second,

the supervisor could ask a supervisee or trainee to practice several skills in front of a mirror so that they have immediate, visual feedback on facial expressions and whether those expressions are concordant with their statements (e.g., "I care about collaboratively selecting meaningful goals for services" accompanied by an earnest and pleasant expression). The supervisee or trainee could also score their own behavior from a video of their performance during role-plays or live interactions with clients. Additional instructional strategies are described in column 4 of Table 5 in Taylor et al. (2019).

Use the reflection activities in the table below to help the NS or their trainees or to support your own skills in developing and maintaining therapeutic relationships.

Reflection	Action
✓ Think about the benefits of asking clients, supervisees, and trainees about their priorities and how those can be integrated into services.	✓ Review the relevant standards (2.09, 2.14, and 3.14) from the Ethics Code for Behavior Analysts (BACB, 2020).
✓ Use the self-assessments in LeBlanc, Sellers et al. (2020) to reflect on your use of therapeutic relationship skills with clients, caregivers, supervisees, and trainees.	✓ Make a list of phrases that can convey caring and empathy in interactions with clients, caregivers, supervisees, and trainees.
✓ Think about what principles of behavior analysis are involved in building a strong relationship with a client, caregiver, supervisee, and trainee.	✓ Identify strategies you could use to repair a therapeutic relationship that is currently not going well.
✓ Think about how one's own covert behavior (e.g., dreading a conversation with someone, feeling relieved when someone stops pushing to convey their priorities) can lead to destructive overt behavior (e.g., cutting someone off, pushing your own agenda, canceling meetings and sessions).	✓ Practice an upcoming conversation with a client, caregiver, supervisee, or trainee in which you might need to apologize, reestablish trust or motivation for services, or set appropriate boundaries.
	✓ Identify a mentor, supervisor, or trusted colleague who excels at these skills and approach them for guidance.

Resources

1. Fiske, K. E. (2017). *Autism and the family: Understanding and supporting parents and siblings.* Norton.

2. LeBlanc, L. A., Sellers, T. P., & Ala'i, S. (2020). *Building and sustaining meaningful and effective relationships as a supervisor and mentor.* Sloan Publishing.

3. LeBlanc, L. A., Taylor, B. A., & Marchese N. V. (2019). The training experiences of behavior analysts: Compassionate care and therapeutic relationships with caregivers. *Behavior Analysis in Practice,* 13, 387–393. https://doi.org/10.1007/s40617-019-00368-z

4. Stewart, John (Ed.) (1999). *Bridges not walls: A book about interpersonal communication.* 7th Ed. McGraw-Hill.

5. Stone, D., Patton, B. & Heen, S. (1999). *Difficult conversations: How to discuss what matters most.* Penguin Books.

6. Taylor, B. A., LeBlanc, L. A., & Nosik, M.R. (2019). Compassionate care in behavior analytic treatment: Can outcomes be enhanced by attending to relationships with caregivers? *Behavior Analysis in Practice,* 12, 654–666. https://org/10.1007/s40617-018-0089-3

7. R. (2019). Compassionate care in behavior analytic treatment: Can outcomes be enhanced by attending to relationships with caregivers? *Behavior Analysis in Practice,* 12, 654–666. https://org/10.1007/s40617-018-0089-3

8. Tulgan, B. (2015). *Bridging the soft skills gap: How to teach the missing basics to today's young talent.* Jossey-Bass.

Enhancing Learning: Self-Monitoring, Describing, and Asking Meaningful Questions

What These Are

There are at least three active-learning skills that you can teach your supervisees and trainees that can enhance continued learning: self-monitoring, self-narrating (i.e., describing your own actions), and asking meaningful questions. Active learning, as opposed to passive observing and listening, can enhance learning throughout supervision. *Self-monitoring* refers to carefully attending to your own behavior, including actions, facial expressions, thoughts and feelings, and stimuli correlated with those behaviors (e.g., others' facial expressions, body language, and vocal responses) (LeBlanc, Sellers et al., 2020). Those responses can then be evaluated against a criterion to determine whether the behavior needs to change (Bandura, 1997). They can also be examined in order to find the functional determinants of your own performance. *Self-narrating* refers to carefully and precisely 1) describing your own actions while doing them or immediately afterward, 2) indicating what was or was not satisfactory about your performance and why, and 3) indicating what needs improvement and why (LeBlanc, Sellers et al., 2020). *Asking meaningful questions* refers to formulating your thoughts before communicating to a supervisor, manager, or colleague so that questions specify the information that is needed and illustrate what you have already done or thought through. It takes thoughtful preparation to ask a meaningful question and supervision presents the perfect opportunity to establish this skill.

Why They Are Important

When we develop robust repertoires for active learning, we increase the chances that we will be able to continue to learn and evolve our skills once we operate independently (i.e., without supervision). These skills help a person evaluate their own performance as well as the variables that are influencing their performance at any given time. Once we can simultaneously behave and evaluate our own behavior, we can rapidly correct our own behavior and learn from our mistakes more quickly and effectively. We are also likely to have a fuller understanding of why we should make certain clinical choices rather than simply following rules or previously observed examples. These skills also allow a person to make the most out of the time that they spend in continuing education or with a supervisor or consultant. Finally, these skills enhance our ability to evaluate our own scope of competence and to potentially expand that scope of competence through observations and interactions with experts.

Assessing These Skills

Each of these skills can be assessed in the context of supervised or independent practice. The best way to assess self-monitoring skills is to directly compare data collected on one's own behavior to data collected by an independent observer. When using self-monitoring as a therapeutic intervention, the first step is always to teach and reinforce accurate data collection. The same approach can be taken with supervisees and trainees. One of the most direct ways to assess a person's skills in performing and narrating their actions is to have them engage in a well-learned skill and collect data on 1) the speed of the skill compared to when they are not self-narrating, 2) the accuracy of the skill compared to when they are not self-narrating, and 3) the amount of detail in the narrative description. Additionally, you can ask them the questions about their performance that illustrate whether they are able to identify decision points and desired outcomes. Finally, questions that are posed in supervision can be scored with respect to the extent to which they match the definition of *a meaningful question* and guide the supervisor's actions rather than taking the form of a statement (e.g., I don't understand this) or simple request for help (e.g., Can you help me find a resource?).

Skill Level	New BCBA	Supervisees/Trainees
Not yet acquired	✓ Unable to accurately score their own performance in a task. ✓ Infrequently or never performs and narrates actions without disruption to performance. ✓ Unable to describe the risks of not evaluating whether a perceived expert is actually an expert. ✓ Infrequently or never accurately describes a desired outcome for an observed sequence. ✓ Infrequently or never accurately identifies decision points in an observed performance. ✓ Information is usually sought by making statements (e.g., "I don't understand") rather than asking meaningful questions.	✓ Unable to accurately score their own performance in a task. ✓ Infrequently or never accurately describes how they would or did complete a task. ✓ Infrequently or never accurately identifies decision points in an observed performance. ✓ Frequently or always requires someone else to point out when their performance is not accurate or sufficient. ✓ Information is usually sought by making statements (e.g., "I don't understand") rather than asking meaningful questions.

(Continues on next page)

Skill Level	New BCBA	Supervisees/Trainees
Developing	✓ Frequently scores their own performance on a task with accuracy as they complete the task.	✓ Able to accurately score their own performance in a task as they complete the task.
	✓ Frequently describes an observed sequence of events with accuracy.	✓ Frequently describes how they would or did complete a task with accuracy.
	✓ Frequently determines whether the observed sequence resulted in the desired outcome.	✓ Frequently identifies decision points in an observed performance with accuracy.
	✓ Frequently describes why an observed response occurred rather than a different response.	✓ Frequently identifies when their performance is not accurate or sufficient.
	✓ Frequently identifies decision points that occurred during the observed performance and why each decision was made.	✓ Frequently seeks information by asking meaningful questions focused on gaining information or evaluating own performance.
	✓ Frequently performs a task at normal speed while narrating actions.	
	✓ Frequently asks meaningful questions focused on gaining information or evaluating own performance.	

Teaching These Skills

A supervisor can teach these skills by modeling each one. For example, when a supervisor performs a task and subsequently *debriefs* (i.e., describes what they did, why they did it, whether they encountered any decision points and why they made the decision that they did), they are modeling delayed narration of their task. They can also model simultaneous self-narration if the audible narration will not affect client services. Prior to or after modeling, the supervisor can explain why they narrate their actions and how it can be helpful to do so in your professional activities.

A supervisor can also take a structured didactic approach to teaching these skills. For example, a supervisor could describe their criteria for a meaningful question and provide examples and non-examples. They could subsequently provide feedback on the questions that are brought to supervision with an opportunity to restate any questions that don't meet the criteria. For self-monitoring and self-narrating, the supervisor could assign Chapter 6 of LeBlanc, Sellers et al., (2020) along with self-monitoring and self-narrating tasks. The supervisor can have the supervisee select a skill that they can already do well and have them narrate their actions (LeBlanc, Sellers et al., 2020). Selecting an intact skill will minimize the chances that narrating disrupts the performance, but initial attempts at self-narration may still slow performance or create errors, so select the skill wisely. If this happens, the person can practice narration while they are viewing video footage of their prior performance.

If the practice occurs during live performance,

the supervisor can have the supervisee perform the skill at a slightly slower-than-typical pace and simultaneously narrate the steps in the response as they are performed (LeBlanc, Sellers et al., 2020). Once the supervisee can vocally narrate the discrete responses or behavior, the supervisor can teach the supervisee to add a narration of their private events (i.e., "Describe what you are doing and what thoughts you are having about your performance"). Next, the supervisor can have the supervisee narrate any decision points that occur and why they made the decisions that they did.

Reflection	Action
✓ Think about the role of careful attending in observational learning.	✓ Review the relevant standards (5.10) from the Ethics Code for Behavior Analysts (BACB, 2020).
✓ Think about the role of curiosity in asking meaningful questions.	✓ Identify an expert and a popular non-expert in the same area. Describe the differences in their behavior, statements, and recommendations.
✓ Think about the processes involved in engaging in an action and simultaneously narrating that action overtly or covertly.	✓ Practice performing and narrating actions and choices until fluent.
✓ Think about the consequences of failing to notice decision points in your applied practice.	✓ Write meaningful questions prior to your supervision sessions and include them in your agenda.
✓ Identify a time when you observed an expert's performance but failed to fully understand what you were observing and why it was occurring.	✓ Observe an expert and ask curious and meaningful questions about their actions and choice during the performance.

Resources

1. LeBlanc, L. A., Sellers, T. P., & Ala'i, S. (2020). *Building and sustaining meaningful and effective relationships as a supervisor and mentor*. Sloan Publishing. Chapter 6

Evaluating Effects of Supervision

What This Is

Evaluating the effects of one's supervisory practices involves collecting and evaluating data to determine if those practices are producing the desired outcomes (LeBlanc, Sellers et al., 2020; Sellers, Valentino, et al., 2016; Turner et al., 2016). Evaluations should take place for each trainee throughout the supervisory relationship. Data should be considered from a variety of sources such as the trainee's performance and feedback, client performance, and caregiver and peer feedback. Supervisors should also evaluate the outcomes across multiple supervisory relationships to ensure that their practices are consistently effective over time and for a variety of trainees. For more guidance on how and what to evaluate, see recommendations in Chapter 10 of LeBlanc, Sellers et al. (2020) and the articles by Sellers, Valentino, et al. (2016) and Turner et al. (2016).

Why This Is Important

Certified behavior analysts are required to take an active role in continually assessing the outcomes of their supervisory practices and strengthening related repertoires through professional learning opportunities. Specifically, standard 4.02 Supervisory Competence (BACB, 2020), states: "Behavior analysts supervise and train others only within their identified scope of competence. They provide supervision only after obtaining knowledge and skills in effective supervisory practices, and they continually evaluate and improve their supervisory repertoires through professional development." (p. 15). The function of this standard is to hold supervisors accountable for demonstrating that they and their trainees are achieving the targeted outcomes. This is critical for many reasons, including being able to replicate positive effects, identify and respond to any deficiencies to protect clients and trainees, and increase the likelihood that trainees will be successful in their future clinical and supervisory endeavors.

Assessing This Skill

One of the most direct ways to assess a supervisor's skills in this area is to simply ask them how they are evaluating the outcomes of their supervisory practices. A competent supervisor will outline the different sources of data and frequency with which they engage in such evaluation. If a full and well-structured response is not immediately produced, that is a good indicator that the supervisor needs to develop their skills in this area. A more in-depth assessment includes reviewing the sources of the supervisor's evaluation. For example, it will be important to review any formal-feedback forms that the individual is using, as well as evidence that the feedback is regularly sought, reviewed, and responded to in a meaningful way. Other resources to review the supervisor include documentation that they have regularly scheduled self-evaluations in their calendar and that they are actively collecting, reviewing, and responding to data from a variety of sources.

Use the indicators on the following page to identify where a new BCBA's or supervisee/trainee's skills fall. For supervisees (e.g., RBTs, BCaBAs) this will only be relevant if they provide supervision to others, and expectations should be adjusted for their skill level. For trainees, this will likely be relevant toward the end of the fieldwork experience, as they take on more responsibilities and move closer to becoming an independent clinician and supervisor. For both supervisees and trainees, their evaluation of their supervisory practices should always be facilitated and overseen by a supervisor.

Skill Level	New BCBA	Supervisees/Trainees
Not yet acquired	✓ Infrequently or never describes the importance of evaluating the outcomes of one's supervisory practices. ✓ Infrequently or never describes the risks of not evaluating the outcomes of one's supervisory practices. ✓ Infrequently or never describes a variety of data sources. ✓ Infrequently or never solicits feedback and guidance about their supervisory practices. ✓ Infrequently or never receives feedback in an appropriate manner (e.g., gets defensive, shuts down). ✓ Infrequently or never implements changes based on feedback and data indicating that their supervisory practices are ineffective.	✓ Same
Developing	✓ Able to provide some indicators of the importance of evaluating one's supervisory practices. ✓ Able to describe some of the risks of not evaluating the outcomes of one's supervisory practices. ✓ Able to describe some data sources. ✓ Can describe why it is important to respond to feedback and data indicating that their supervisory practices are ineffective. ✓ Frequently solicits feedback and guidance about their supervisory practices. ✓ Frequently receives feedback in an appropriate manner (e.g., actively listens, makes statements of appreciation and accountability). ✓ Frequently implements changes based on feedback and data indicating that their supervisory practices are ineffective.	✓ Same

Teaching This Skill

Evaluating the effects of one's supervisory practices relies on a variety of component skills (e.g., data collection, soliciting feedback, evaluating data, having crucial conversations, self-management); therefore, it can be helpful to teach these component skills individually early on so that they can then be leveraged together to support this evaluation. Mentors and supervisors can facilitate the growth of these skills in new BCBAs and trainees by clearly describing the process and why it is important. Modeling and guided practice are likely to be effective strategies for teaching and strengthening the repertoires needed to carry out an evaluation of one's supervisory practices. This can be done by showing the new BCBA or trainee the types of data to collect, examples of data collection and feedback forms, how to create their own capture systems, and by walking them through the process of reviewing and responding to the data collected. It may also be critical to highlight other useful prompts like recurring calendar reminders and related tasks on their curricular roadmaps for their supervisees and trainees.

Use the reflection activities together with your CS (for you), or trainees (for them), or by yourself to support your skills in evaluating and identifying your scope of competence. Similarly, the actions can be used together with your CS to facilitate your skills, by you with your trainees to develop their skills, or on your own to independently work on your own skills.

Reflection	Action
✓ Think about the benefits of continually evaluating the effects of one's supervisory practices and the risks of failing to do so.	✓ Review the relevant standards (1.05, 1.06, and 4.02) from the Ethics Code for Behavior Analysts (BACB, 2020).
✓ Think about what dimensions of behavior analysis are related to engaging in this evaluation.	✓ Make a list of the sources of data that should be evaluated.
✓ Think about the processes involved in programming for clients and how those same practices can be leveraged to evaluate the outcomes of supervisory practices.	✓ Identify how frequently the different sources of data should be collected and evaluated; (note that the schedule should be more frequently for newer supervisors and at the outset of any relationship).
✓ Think about how one's own covert behavior (e.g., dreading or looking forward to supervision meetings, feeling relieved or disappointed when meetings are cancelled) and overt behavior (e.g., disengaged or engaged in meetings, frequently canceling meetings) can be used to support this evaluation.	✓ Find or create needed forms.
	✓ Practice conversations for soliciting feedback from supervisees, caregivers, peers, etc.
✓ Think about how soliciting, receiving, implementing, and providing feedback can positively or negatively impact the supervisory relationship.	✓ Identify a mentor, supervisor, or trusted colleague with more supervisory experience with whom you can review and evaluate the data collected.

Resources

1. Behavior Analyst Certification Board. (2020). *Ethics code for behavior analysts.* Littleton, CO: Author.

2. LeBlanc, L. A., Sellers, T. P., & Ala'i, S. (2020). *Building and sustaining meaningful and effective relationships as a supervisor and mentor.* Sloan Publishing.

3. Sellers, T. P., Valentino, A. L., & LeBlanc, L. A. (2016). Recommended practices for individual supervision of aspiring behavior analysts. *Behavior Analysis in Practice, 9*(4), 274-286.

4. Turner, L. B., Fischer, A. J., & Luiselli, J. K. (2016). Towards a competency-based, ethical, and socially valid approach to the supervision of applied behavior-analytic trainees. *Behavior Analysis in Practice, 9*(4), 287-298.

Feedback and Difficult Conversations

What These Are

Feedback is not only one of the most frequently used interventions to impact performance in human-service settings (Gravina et al., 2018), it has been demonstrated to be a critical component of BST (Ward-Horner & Sturmey, 2012). For our purposes, *feedback* is information given to a trainee or supervisee about their past performance that functions to inform their future performance. That is, feedback can be specific praise that identifies what the trainee did well that results in them performing the skill in that same manner in the future. Feedback can also be specific information identifying what was problematic about their performance and what they should do in the future to improve. In the literature there are sub-types of feedback (e.g., adequacy, diagnostic, corrective, supportive) which can be helpful when measuring or teaching about feedback. LeBlanc, Sellers et al. (2020) provide descriptions of the main sub-types of feedback (e.g., adequacy, diagnostic, corrective, supportive) in chapter 5 of their book.

In practice, several considerations are related to feedback. One set of considerations focuses the parameters of feedback (e.g., timing, magnitude, order, ratio of positive to corrective) for an individual (chapters 2 and 5 in LeBlanc, Sellers et al, 2020). The parameters of feedback can, and should, be individualized for the recipient and context. The other set of considerations has to do with the larger classes of feedback skills needed to be a successful clinician and supervisor—soliciting, receiving, implementing, and giving feedback. Each of those components rely on slightly different but interrelated skills. For example, giving feedback requires skills related to perspective taking, in the moment discrimination, decision making, and interpersonal communication, to name a few. Implementing feedback, on the other hand, requires not only discrimination skills, but also self-reflection, evaluation, and management skills. Supervisors must also document feedback provided and effectively teach the components related to feedback to their trainees and supervisees.

In addition to general feedback skills, it is inevitable that BCBAs will have to have difficult conversations with supervisees, trainees, caregivers, colleagues, and other professionals. In the book *Crucial Conversations*, the authors define *crucial* (aka difficult) *conversations* as those that focus on something important or critical, involve differences of opinions, and wherein emotions run high (Grenny et al., 2022). Chapter 9 in the book by LeBlanc, Sellers et al. (2020) covers interpersonal and therapeutic relations skills and provides many helpful strategies for increasing the quality of communication skills, particularly related to difficult topics. Some examples of crucial conversations for BCBAs include conversations when providing critical corrective feedback, during a discussion addressing that feedback has not been implemented, when disagreeing about treatment options.

Why They Are Important

Effective repertoires related to feedback are critical to successfully teaching and shaping supervisees' and trainees' performance. Providing and teaching high-quality feedback to supervisees and trainees can:

1. improve their clinical performance,
2. build their repertoires to be successful supervisors,
3. increase positive outcomes for clients, and
4. create and maintain a positive supervisory relationship.

Alternatively, providing low-quality feedback, or avoiding it altogether, can result in the development of defective or harmful clinical and supervisory repertoires for the supervisee or trainee, harm to clients, and damage to the supervisory relationship. Therefore, it is critical the supervisors develop well-rounded repertoires for giving, soliciting, receiving, implementing, documenting feedback, as well as expressly teaching all the components to their trainees.

Difficult or crucial conversations are important because many of us have not been explicitly taught the skills necessarily to navigate them successfully. Many of us tend to avoid them, which can lead to a worsening of the problem and even direct risks of harm. Others of us may address them, but not in a skilled and purposeful manner. For example, we may be so indirect that the listener cannot discriminate that we are providing feedback about their performance. Alternatively, we may be so direct that we create such an aversive experience that prevents the listener from being able to receive the critical information about their performance. In either of these extremes, it is unlikely that the individual's performance will change, and we may damage the supervisory relationship.

Assessing These Skills

Feedback and difficult conversation skills can be assessed through discussion, case-examples, role-play, and observation. For example, these skills could be tested by role-playing or watching video examples of feedback delivery and asking the individual to score or describe 1) what went well and why, 2) what did not go well and why, and 3) what should be done to correct the issue. Assessments should include multiple exemplars across contexts and feedback components. For example, it is likely insufficient to only assess an individual's ability to give feedback and not assess their ability to solicit, receive, implement, and document feedback. Similarly, evaluating an individual's ability to provide high-quality feedback to an RBT while failing to evaluate their ability in relation to caregivers, colleagues, and other professionals probably results in an incomplete picture of their skills.

Skill Level	New BCBA	Supervisees/Trainees

Not yet acquired	✓ Unable to describe:
	  ◦ the function of feedback.
	  ◦ the components of high-quality feedback.
	  ◦ the risks of low-quality of feedback or failure to provide feedback.
	  ◦ strategies for soliciting feedback.
	  ◦ strategies for implementing feedback.
	  ◦ strategies for navigating difficult conversations.
	
	✓ Unable to effectively:
	  ◦ role-play delivering, receiving, or teaching feedback.
	  ◦ teach others skills related to feedback.
	
	✓ Consistent difficulty with or avoidance of giving, soliciting, receiving, implementing, and documenting feedback or having difficult conversations.
		✓ Difficulty receiving and implementing feedback.
		
		✓ Difficulty with, or absence of giving feedback to supervisor.
		
		✓ Difficulty with, or absence of soliciting feedback from supervisor.

Developing	✓ Able to describe some components of high-quality feedback and difficult conversations (listed above). ✓ Able to engage in role-play and discussions with some success. ✓ Frequently gives, solicits, receives, implements, and documents feedback and has some difficult conversations with some success.	✓ Some success receiving and implementing feedback. ✓ Some success with, or attempts to give feedback to supervisor. ✓ Some success with, or attempts to solicit feedback from supervisor.

Teaching These Skills

These skills should be expressly taught, using Behavioral Skills Training (BST). Discussions should include multiple exemplars, the benefits related to high-quality feedback and engaging in difficult conversations, as well as the risks of low-quality feedback, no feedback, and avoiding difficult conversations. A supervisor could use written descriptions or movie clips depicting things like feedback solicitation, reception, delivery, or a difficult conversation and role-plays to teach these skills. After a model or role-play, an individual should engage in the same three steps described in the assessment section. In instances where the feedback delivery or difficult conversations needed to be corrected, the individual could subsequently role-play a corrected version and then debrief about the improvements and if they were successful. Individuals can be provided with samples of lists of the critical components of feedback delivery and reception; scripts for giving, soliciting and soliciting feedback; scripts for navigating difficult conversations; feedback solicitation and documentation forms; and checklists for teaching each of these skills to practice and use. See the resources list for valuable articles and books to facilitate teaching skills related to feedback delivery and navigating difficult conversations. There are many helpful resources in the LeBlanc, Sellers et al. (2020) book, including those referenced below:

- Chapter 2 Activity: Exploring Collaboration Topics p. 24

- Chapter 2 Appendix: How to Talk About Feedback p. 26

- Chapter 5 Table with examples of how to convert feedback statements p. 87

- Chapter 5 Appendix C: Script for Explaining Feedback and Responding to Feedback p. 94

- Chapter 11 Case Example 2: A Supervisor's Harsh Feedback p. 223

Use the reflection activities together with your CS (for you), or trainees (for them), or by yourself to support your skills in evaluating and identifying your scope of competence. Similarly, the actions can be used together with your CS to facilitate your skills, by you with your trainees to develop their skills, or on your own to independently work on your own skills.

Reflection	Action
✓ Think about your past experiences giving and receiving feedback or having difficult conversations and what the outcomes were. ✓ Think about how your supervisees and trainees (and others) respond to your feedback or difficult conversations. ✓ Think about past instances where you avoided providing feedback to, or having difficult conversations with a supervisor, supervisee, trainee, or other individual: 　◦ Why do you think you avoided it? 　◦ What was the outcome? ✓ Think about a time when you are pretty sure that someone did not provide you with feedback or have a difficult conversation with you that could have helped you improve: 　◦ Why do you think they avoided it? 　◦ What was the outcome?	✓ Write out some of the statements you typically use to give different types of feedback or navigate difficult conversations and then edit them for improvement (e.g., more compassionate, objective, specific). ✓ Write out some common specific feedback and difficult conversation scenarios to practice with yourself and use in your supervision. ✓ Start collecting video examples of high-quality and low-quality feedback and difficult conversations from movies and shows to use in your supervision. ✓ Develop a list of critical components for high-quality feedback and difficult conversations to use in your supervision for scoring yourself and for teaching trainees. ✓ Review your forms for soliciting feedback and edit for improvement. ✓ Access the articles and books in the resource list and calendar time to review each, discuss with colleagues, and create follow-up tasks.

Resources

1. Ehrlich, R. J., Nosik, M. R., Carr, J. E., & Wine, B. (2020). Teaching employees how to receive feedback: A preliminary investigation. *Journal of Organizational Behavior Management, 40*(1-2), 19-29.

2. Gravina, N., Villacorta, J., Albert, K., Clark, R., Curry, S., & Wilder, D. (2018). A literature review of organizational behavior management interventions in human service settings from 1990 to 2016. *Journal of Organizational Behavior Management, 38*(23), 191–224. doi:10.1080/01608061.2018.1454872

3. Grenny, J., Patterson, K., McMillan, R., Switzler, A., & Gregory, E. (2022). *Crucial conversations: Tools for talking when stakes are high* (3rd ed.). McGraw Hill.

4. Kazemi, E., Rice, B., & Adzhyan, P. (2018). *Fieldwork and supervision for behavior analysts: A handbook.* Springer Publishing Company.

5. LeBlanc, L. A., Sellers, T. P., & Ala'i, S. (2020). *Building and sustaining meaningful and effective relationships as a supervisor and mentor.* Sloan Publishing.

6. Scott, K. (2019). *Radical Candor: Be a kick-ass boss without losing your humanity (fully revised & updated ed.).* St. Martin's Press.

7. Sellers, T. P., LeBlanc, L. A., & Valentino, A. L. (2016). Recommendations for detecting and addressing barriers to successful supervision. *Behavior Analysis in Practice, 9*(4), 309-319.

8. Sellers, T. P., Valentino, A. L., & LeBlanc, L. A. (2016). Recommended practices for individual supervision of aspiring behavior analysts. *Behavior Analysis in Practice, 9*(4), 274-286.

9. Stone, D., Patton, B., & Heen, S. (2010). *Difficult conversations: How to discuss what matters most (10th anniversary ed.).* Penguin Books.

10. Turner, L. B., Fischer, A. J., & Luiselli, J. K. (2016). Towards a competency-based, ethical, and socially valid approach to the supervision of applied behavior-analytic trainees. *Behavior Analysis in Practice, 9*(4), 287-298.

11. Walker, S., & Sellers, T. (2021). Teaching appropriate feedback reception skills using computer-based instruction: A systematic replication. *Journal of Organizational Behavior Management,* 1-19.

12. Ward-Horner, J., & Sturmey, P. (2012). Component analysis of behavior skills training in functional analysis. *Behavioral Interventions, 27*(2), 75–92.

Ongoing Monitoring and Performance Management

What These Are

Ongoing monitoring refers to the continual review and evaluation of services delivered to someone, whether that is a client, a supervisee, or a trainee. Typically, ongoing monitoring of clinical programming involves collecting and reviewing data on the acquisition and reductive programming in place to identify the degree to which the desired outcomes are being achieved, and to make timely decisions related to those data. For example, a client who is making consistent and rapid progress will require introducing new targets and programs and a client who is not demonstrating maintenance of previously mastered skills may require adjustments to instructional strategies and mastery criteria. When we talk about ongoing monitoring and *performance management* of supervisees and trainees, we are generally referring to observing the performance of skills the supervisee or trainee is learning or has learned, collecting and evaluating data, and providing any needed coaching. As with clients, consistent review of their performance allows a supervisor to:

1. ensure they are implementing skills and carrying out tasks accurately;

2. assess progress, maintenance, and generalization; and

3. identify needs, make decisions, and implement adjustments in a timely manner (Parsons et al., 2012).

If any performance needs are detected, supervisors can immediately provide feedback, coaching, or additional training. If the supervisor is unsuccessful in addressing the performance need, they can implement a functional assessment, such as the Performance Diagnostic Checklist – Human Services (PDC-HS; Carr et al., 2013) of the contextual barriers and develop a well-matched, performance-improvement plan for the supervisee or trainee.

Why They Are Important

Failing to engage in ongoing monitoring of clients, supervisees, and trainees, can negatively impact progress, invite risks of harm, and result in wasted time and resources (LeBlanc, Sellers et al., 2020). For supervisees and trainees, failing to implement ongoing monitoring and performance management of their acquisition can also result in them feeling unsupported, questioning their abilities, or assuming that they are doing well when that might not be the case. If there are performance issues, particularly those that are resistant to initial feedback, failing to implement performance management can worsen the issue and invite risk of harm to clients and others. Taking a structured approach to performance management that includes collecting data, goal setting, and planning structured supports allows the supervisor to carefully monitor the effects of the plan and make systematic adjustments as needed.

Assessing These Skills

New BCBAs and more advanced trainees should be engaging in ongoing monitoring and performance management of clients, supervisees, and trainees. Having a discussion with the individual wherein you ask specific questions can be helpful in evaluating their level of knowledge and skill related to ongoing monitoring. Some questions include "What is ongoing monitoring or performance management?" "Why is it important to engage in ongoing monitoring or performance management?" "What are some ways to engage in ongoing monitoring of clients, supervisees, and trainees and performance management of supervisees and trainees?" These skills can be assessed by asking to see the schedule for ongoing monitoring and the practices used (e.g., reviewing data, observing, collecting satisfaction feedback). It may be the case that an individual engages in ongoing monitoring of clients but *not* of their supervisees or trainees, which is an indication of a failure to generalize the skill. Another method of assessment is to provide case scenarios and ask the individual to identify on

what schedule they would engage in ongoing monitoring or performance management, how they would do so, and what they would look for in their monitoring, and what they would do to address any issues. When using case scenarios to assess skills related to performance management, the focus should be on assessing if they can clearly identify the performance issue, evaluate the contributing environmental barriers, and outline a performance-management plan to address the issue, or indicate that they would use a structured tool, such as the PDC-HS (Carr et al., 2013). See articles by Garza et al. (2018), Sellers, LeBlanc et al. (2016), and Sellers, Valentino et al. (2016) for considerations and resources to assist in assessing these skills.

Use the indicators listed below to assess skills related to ongoing monitoring and performance management.

Skill Level	New BCBA	Supervisees/Trainees
Not yet acquired	✓ Unable to describe ongoing monitoring and performance management and why they are important for clinical programming and supervising others. ✓ Unable to describe strategies for engaging ongoing monitoring for clinical programming and supervisees. ✓ Unable to describe strategies for performance management of staff. ✓ Infrequently or never identifies present or emerging clinical or performance issues in a timely manner or at all.	✓ Unable to describe ongoing monitoring and why it is important for clinical programming. ✓ Unable to describe strategies for engaging ongoing monitoring of clinical programming. ✓ Infrequently or never detects possible needs in clinical programming in a timely manner or at all. ✓ Infrequently or never alerts supervisor of possible needs in clinical programming in a timely manner.

Skill Level	New BCBA	Supervisees/Trainees
Developing	✓ Able to provide some description of ongoing monitoring and performance management and why they are important for clinical programming and supervising others. ✓ Able to describe and frequently implements some strategies for ongoing monitoring of clinical programming and supervisees. ✓ Able to describe and frequently implements some strategies for performance management of staff. ✓ Frequently identifies present or emerging clinical or performance issues.	✓ Able to provide some description of ongoing monitoring and why it is important for clinical programming. ✓ Able to describe and frequently implements some strategies for ongoing monitoring of clinical programming. ✓ Frequently detects some possible needs in clinical programming in a timely manner. ✓ Frequently alerts supervisor of possible needs in clinical programming in a timely manner.

Teaching These Skills

BST can be used to teach the practice of ongoing monitoring and performance management, with heavy use of role-play and supported practice. In addition, BST should include multiple exemplars that represent the conditions likely to be present in the natural environment. For example, present the individual with a variety of learner and performer profiles and patterns. For clients, this might include learner profiles along a continuum of complexity (e.g., absence or presence of other health needs, severe problem behavior, communication needs, fine and gross motor needs, sensory deficits) and learner patterns (e.g., slow acquisition, fast acquisition, variable responding, failure to acquire certain types of programs, plateauing, failure to maintain or generalize skills). For supervisees and trainees, the case examples may include some of those same learning patterns and some different patterns of responding (e.g., argumentative, difficult or failure accepting and/or implementing feedback). Teach using a functional-

assessment approach to persistent issues, such as how to implement the PDC-HS (Carr et al., 2013) and develop a matched plan to support the individual and improve their performance. Use case scenarios and practice completing the PDC-HS, draft-matched plans, and discuss what they would monitor to evaluate if the plan was successful and what they would do if it was not. The articles in the resource list provide recommendations and guidance for addressing these skills.

The reflection and actions items on the following page can be using in building skills related to ongoing monitoring and performance management.

Reflection	Action
✓ Reflect on why it is critical to engage in ongoing monitoring of clinical programming and supervision (e.g., risk, benefits).	✓ Create a schedule for clients, supervisees, and trainees for ongoing progress-monitoring (i.e., when should you expect to see improvements and how will you check?).
✓ Reflect on why it is critical to engage in performance management of supervisees and trainees.	✓ Create a form for conducting ongoing progress-monitoring for clients, supervisees, and trainees.

✓ Reflect on any past experiences where clinical issues or performance issues were not detected in a timely manner:
  ◦ What were the outcomes?
  ◦ How could the issue or need have been identified earlier?
	✓ Create a list of critical-performance indicators for supervisees and trainees (e.g., timeliness, accuracy in data and billing records, confidentiality, safety, client respect and dignity) and begin to create performance monitoring and integrity forms.

✓ Reflect on a time when performance issues were identified in a trainee or supervisee but were not systematically addressed:
  ◦ Did the issue improve or worsen?
  ◦ What were the negative impacts?
	✓ Create a policy and resources (e.g., formal-feedback documentation, performance improvement plan templates) for addressing persistent performance issues.

	✓ Create scripts for discussing performance management of persistent performance issues.

Resources

1. Carr, J. E., Wilder, D. A., Majdalany, L., Mathisen, D., & Strain, L. A. (2013). An assessment-based solution to a human-service employee-performance problem. *Behavior Analysis in Practice, 6*, 16–32.

2. Garza, K. L., McGee, H. M., Schenk, Y. A., & Wiskirchen, R. R. (2018). Some tools for carrying out a proposed process for supervising experience hours for aspiring Board-Certified Behavior Analysts®. *Behavior Analysis in Practice, 11*, 62–70.

3. Parsons, M. B., Rollyson, J. H., & Reid, D. H. (2012). Evidence-based staff training. *Behavior Analysis in Practice, 5*, 2–11. doi: 10.1007/BF03391819

4. Sellers, T. P., LeBlanc, L. A. & Valentino, A. V. (2016). Recommendations for detecting and addressing barriers to successful supervision. *Behavior Analysis in Practice, 9*, 309–319. doi: 10.1007/s40617-016- 0142-z

5. Sellers, T. P., Valentino, A. L., & LeBlanc, L. A. (2016). Recommended practices for individual supervision of aspiring behavior analysts. *Behavior Analysis in Practice, 9*, 274–286. doi:10.1007/s40617-016- 0110-7

Organizational Skills and Time Management

What These Are

Organizational skills refer to planning and prioritizing activities and projects, goal setting, and organizing materials so that they are easy to find when needed. Managing emails, electronic calendars, and electronic file storage and sharing systems are critical skills for success in today's practice environment. *Time management* refers to planning the use of available time in line with priorities, personal goals and lifestyles, and professional demands (LeBlanc, Sellers et al., 2020). For example, a new BCBA must learn how to manage all the tasks associated with effectively managing their caseload (e.g., assessment, report writing, selecting goals, writing programs, analyzing data and modifying programs, providing supervision, meeting with parents) efficiently or many of these tasks may be neglected or pushed into non-work time (e.g., evenings, weekends). Managing meetings is a subskill in this area that becomes increasingly important as a trainee transitions into independent practice and supervising others. Leading meetings effectively requires advanced planning and creation of an agenda and management of time during the meeting to accomplish the tasks included on the agenda (LeBlanc & Nosik, 2019).

Why They Are Important

LeBlanc, Sellers et al. (2020) refers to these skills as pivotal as they set the upper limit of what a person can achieve with their other skill sets. These skills allow a person to achieve goals in the minimum time possible through planning and self-management.

They are also critical for managing stress while remaining productive (Allen, 2015). These skills have been shown to be related to successful transition into the workforce in practice-related disciplines (Ervin, 2008).

Unfortunately, poor time-management skills can result in increased stress and depression, procrastination, and difficulties in managing job duties. LeBlanc, Sleeper, et al. (2020) found that OTM skills (e.g., explicit use of strategies, efficiency and effectiveness of task completion, proportion of primary activities off task) were the best predictor of success or failure in caseload-management skills for BCBAs. These skills were more predictive of success or failure than other variables that we might expect to matter (e.g., size of caseload, match between client needs and clinical skills, and funding constraints).

Assessing These Skills

LeBlanc, Sellers et al. (2020) Chapter 8, Appendix D provides an assessment of organization and time-management skills. This narrative assessment is a good place to start identifying skills to refine. Allen & Hall (2019) provide an *Assess Your Reality* tool in Chapter 2 of their *Getting Things Done Workbook*. This assessment is scored, and the summed score can be compared to score ranges that indicate your progress on recommended practices for organization and time management. Finally, LeBlanc & Nosik (2019) provide a checklist that can be used to guide meeting planning and management and to evaluate meetings that have already occurred. In addition to these more comprehensive assessments, the following indicators can be used to determine if there may be problems with these skills.

Skill Level	New BCBA	Supervisees/Trainees
Not yet acquired	✓ Does not have a system for scheduling time or does not stick to the schedule that they create. ✓ Does not keep an actions list or write down ideas as soon as they occur. ✓ Frequently or always slow to respond or does not respond to emails, texts, and phone messages. ✓ Frequently or always late to meetings or has to leave in the middle of a task due to overlapping commitments. ✓ Frequently commits to more things than they can actually do. ✓ Infrequently or never creates agendas or manages meeting time to accomplish the things on the agenda.	✓ Same
Developing	✓ Frequently manages time and tasks efficiently. ✓ Frequently keeps track of all assigned tasks and new ideas. ✓ Frequently seeks clarification about tasks. ✓ Frequently breaks down complex tasks into a series of smaller, actionable steps. ✓ Frequently estimates with accuracy how long it will take to accomplish a task. ✓ Frequently accesses information using technology resources in an effective and timely manner. ✓ Frequently manages meeting time well, according to LeBlanc & Nosik (2019) checklist.	✓ Same

Teaching/Refining These Skills

Self-assessment of these skills often produces some degree of insight about problems that have not previously been recognized as such. This is important because interventions for these skills may not be successful if the person does not acknowledge that their skills are sub-par. After self-assessment, a supervisor can teach these skills using BST. A variety of print resource materials on organization and time management are available. One particularly easy one to use is *The Getting Things Done Workbook* (Allen & Hall, 2019).

Reflection	Action
✓ Think about the relationship between stress and organization and time management.	✓ Make a list of your upcoming tasks.
✓ Think about recent tasks that were not completed or were not completed on time and the direct or indirect consequences.	✓ Identify a tool to use to capture your ideas as they come up.
✓ Think about the role of stimulus control in managing task lists and schedules.	✓ Develop and implement a system for triaging and archiving your emails.
✓ Assess your own stress level.	✓ Identify tasks that are often delayed and analyze why these tasks are not completed when they should be.
✓ Assess your strategies using the tools in Allen & Hall (2019).	✓ Identify a mentor, supervisor, or trusted colleague with exceptional organization and time-management skills and interview them about their strategies.

Resources

1. Allen, D. A. (2015). *Getting things done: The art of stress-free productivity*(Revised). Penguin Publishing.

2. LeBlanc, L. A., & Nosik, M. R. (2019). Planning and leading effective meetings. *Behavior Analysis in Practice, 12*, 696–708.

3. LeBlanc, L. A., Sellers, T. P., & Ala'i, S. (2020). *Building and sustaining meaningful and effective relationships as a supervisor and mentor.* Sloan Publishing. Chapter 8

4. LeBlanc, L. A., Sleeper, J. D., Mueller, J. R., Jenkins, S. R., & Harper-Briggs, A. M. (2020). Assessing barriers to effective caseload management by practicing behavior analysts. *Journal of Organizational Behavior Management, 39*(3–4), 317–336.

5. Learn higher. (n.d.). Time management. Retrieved from http://www.learnhigher. ac.uk/learning-at-university/time-management/

6. Lencioni, P. (2004). *Death by meeting.* Jossey-Bass.

7. Mind Tools Content Team. (n.d.) *S.M.A.R.T. Goals: How to make your goals achievable.* Mind tools. https://www. mindtools.com/pages/article/smart-goals.htm

8. Moronz-Alpert, Y. (n.d.) *5 tricks for an efficient morning at work.* Real Simple. http://www.wisnik.com/wp-content/uploads/2014/09/Real-Simple_TM_2014.pdf

9. Princeton University (2016). *Principles of effective time management for balance, well-being, and success.* The McGraw Center for Teaching & Learning. https://mcgraw. princeton.edu/sites/mcgraw/fi les/media/eff ective-time-management.pdf

10. Purdue University Global. (2018, April). *Time management tips for busy college students.* https://www.purdueglobal.edu/blog/student-life/time-management-busy-college-students/

11. Thomack, B. (2012). Time management for today's workplace demands. *Workplace Health & Safety, 60*(5), 201–203. https://doi.org/10.1177/216507991206000503

Problem-Solving and Decision Making

What These Are

These two sets of skills are heavily intertwined. In fact, decision making can be viewed as problem-solving when it is approached in a careful and systematic way. Skinner (1953) defines *problem-solving* as "any behavior which, through the manipulation of variables, makes the appearance of a solution more probable" (p. 584). Problem-solving involves several mediating responses including manipulating, supplementing, and generating stimuli (e.g., visualizing, questioning) to which an individual can subsequently respond (Axe et al., 2019; Donahoe & Palmer, 2004; LeBlanc, Sellers et al., 2020; Skinner, 1953, 1957, 1968). Two common types of responses to problems do not qualify as problem-solving because they do not actually bring one closer to a solution: impulsivity and inactivity/avoidance (LeBlanc, n.d.; LeBlanc, Sellers et al., 2020). The supervisor can help their supervisees and trainees overcome their tendencies to avoid noticing or reporting problems. The supervisor can

1. prompt the supervisee to monitor and report problems early,
2. respond positively when a supervisee reports a potential problem (e.g., praise the detection and report of the problem), and
3. model using a structured problem-solving approach to jointly solve problems.

LeBlanc, Sellers et al. (2020) and LeBlanc (n.d.) outline a five-step, structured problem-solving approach that can be used to make clinical decisions, solve staff performance problems, and tackle potential ethical dilemmas. The five steps should be followed in a systematic progression and the accuracy and effectiveness of performance at each step should be self-monitored. The five steps are

1. detect the problem;
2. define the problem behaviorally;
3. generate solutions;
4. select a solution based on a pro/con analysis; and
5. implement the solution and evaluate the effects.

Step	Skill	Common Problem	Strategy to Increase Effectiveness
Detect the Problem.	Nuanced Noticing— ability to notice subtle changes in behavior or the environment.	Avoidance of early indicators of the problem. Confusing the crisis with the underlying problem.	Careful reflection. Questioning.
Define the Problem.	Identify the functional determinants— A, B, Cs.	Confusing topography with function. Failure to generalize functional assessment skills beyond client problem behavior.	Functional-assessment interview. Performance Diagnostic Checklist.
Generate Potential Solutions.	Brainstorming to produce a large and diverse set of potential solutions.	Lack of variability in response generation. Overuse of strategies that have worked in other situations. No link between solution and functional determinants. Evaluating and dismissing potential solutions (should not occur until step 4).	Brainstorm with two or more people. State expectations and goal for the number of options. Be ambitious with ideas. Change your environment. Specify how the solution addresses the function.
Select a Solution(s).	Conduct a thorough analysis of the short-term and long-term pros and cons of at least two ideas.	Only identifies pros of your own idea or cons of someone else's idea. Overfocuses on short-term pros and cons. Fail to recognize unintended impact of actions on others. No solution is selected due to avoidance (i.e., I need more data, need to keep thinking about it).	Create a chart with short-term and long-term pros and cons. Seek input from those who might be impacted by the decision. Include taking no action as one of the options in your pro/con analysis.
Implement and Evaluate a Solution.	Implementation Planning and Data Collection.	Incomplete implementation planning. No data collection on effects of the solution or on unintended consequences.	Create an implementation plan with a timeline. Identify at least three metrics that might be expected to change based on the implementation.

This structured problem-solving model has been integrated into clinical decision-making models. The models guide the reader through a series of questions about the most common barriers to solution implementation (e.g., safety concerns, lack of resources) and the options that are best suited to overcome those barriers. These models then provide a pro/con analysis that assists the behavior analyst in collaborative decision making with the ultimate implementer (e.g., parent, teacher). For example, LeBlanc, Sellers et al. (2016) describe a model for selecting appropriate measures for assessing and treating problem behavior. The model guides the user through questions about the topography of the behavior, environmental resources, and the importance of temporal dimensions for treatment planning. The answers to the questions in the model lead the user toward the measure(s) that are generally well suited to the needs and constraints of the situation. The table provides a comprehensive pro/con analysis that allows the user to compare each reasonable option for the specific situation. Similarly, Geiger et al. (2010) provide a decision-making model and pro/con analysis for selecting function-based treatments for escape-maintained problem behavior and Grow et al. (2009) provide the same information for attention-maintained problem behavior.

The same structured problem-solving approach can be used to examine and solve ethical problems. LeBlanc, Onofrio et al. (2020) describe the development of an Ethics Network in a human-service organization that was established to help employees conceptualize and respond to ethics scenarios using a structured problem-solving approach. They taught an overarching problem-solving strategy that was broadly applicable to many different ethical dilemmas. Their multistep, structured problem-solving model included six steps, breaking the fifth step described above into two separate steps of implementation and evaluation. Throughout the organization, people were taught to analyze and respond to ethical scenarios using this approach.

Why They Are Important

Having a strong problem-solving repertoire is useful for both personal and professional situations (LeBlanc, Sellers, et al., 2020). Problems cause stress, anxiety, and avoidance in the absence of a framework for analysis and solution generation. Problems can also create the opportunity to hone problem-solving skills and develop confidence that enhances future problem-solving. "The supervisor who focuses on teaching problem-solving skills is programming for the supervisee's future independence and success by teaching them how to solve future problems, rather than simply providing a solution to the current problem" (LeBlanc, Sellers et al., 2020, p. 117). As we practice our problem-solving skills, we can overcome avoidance responses and tackle problems with confidence that we can analyze the problem, generate potential solutions, evaluate the success of the chosen option, and change course if the first solution does not work. The goal of structured collaborative problem-solving during supervision is that the supervisee learns that they should not be afraid if they do not have an immediate answer because they have developed the ability to find those answers through the problem-solving process.

Assessing These Skills

These skills can be assessed via direct observation in structured problem-solving exercises using the problem-solving worksheet from LeBlanc, Sellers et al. (2020). They can also be assessed in vivo as problems arise in the context of ongoing practice and supervision. The trainee can also self-assess their own problem-solving patterns using *Appendix B: Assessing Common Difficulties with Problem Solving* in LeBlanc, Sellers et al. (2020). In addition, here are indicators that will help you assess the skill levels of your trainees or NSs.

Skill Level	New BCBA	Supervisees/Trainees
Not yet acquired	✓ Frequently or always panics or becomes angry when a problem or ethical dilemma is detected.	✓ Has difficulty generating any solutions to a problem.
	✓ Frequently or always has difficulty generating multiple solutions to a problem.	✓ Avoids noticing or reporting problems to supervisor.
	✓ Frequently or always selects solutions and clinical options without conducting a pro/con analysis or identifying the function of the problem.	✓ Same
	✓ Frequently or always avoids noticing problems.	
	✓ Frequently or always avoids making decisions.	
	✓ Is insecure about their decisions.	
	✓ Relies on strategies that they have seen work before even if those strategies are ill-suited to the current context.	
	✓ Cannot describe the variables that should be influencing their choices.	
Developing	✓ Frequently remains calm when a problem is detected.	✓ Same
	✓ Frequently notices problems early.	
	✓ Can successfully complete the 5-step problem-solving process.	
	✓ Frequently generates multiple potential solutions linked to the function of the problem.	
	✓ Can describe the benefits of making a decision even when it is difficult.	
	✓ Can describe what they would do if plan A does not work out.	
	✓ Can describe the variables that should be influencing their clinical choices.	
	✓ Can analyze ethical dilemmas using the problem-solving model.	

Teaching/Refining These Skills

Supervisors who use this structured problem-solving approach in their own work have the perfect opportunity to model the process for their supervisees and trainees across a variety of areas (e.g., staff performance problems, clinical decisions, ethical dilemmas). They can describe the steps while going through them using Chapter 7 Appendix A from LeBlanc, Sellers et al. (2020). The supervisor can explicitly describe that clinical decision making is problem-solving and should be approached in a systematic way and describe prior problem-solving efforts and the results that were obtained. The supervisor can describe common, subtle indicators for emerging problems such as strained therapeutic relationships, blurred boundaries in the relationship with a client and/or family, or staff dissatisfaction with the supervisory process. The supervisor can ask the supervisee open-ended questions about what things make them think that a current situation is going well or going poorly. A supervisor can also use video examples to illustrate subtle behaviors or environmental conditions that might indicate that a problem is brewing.

To teach effective problem definition and function identification, the supervisor can prompt the supervisee or trainee to identify the functional determinants of any problem that they bring to supervision (e.g., clinical problems, ethical concerns, parent-adherence problems). When a supervisee or trainee expresses frustration with staff performance or parent procedural integrity, prompt them to operationalize the problem and then use a tool such as the PDC-HS or the self-assessment of therapeutic relationship skills in Chapter 9 of LeBlanc, Sellers et al. (2020) to examine the problem in terms of the functional determinants. The supervisor might help their supervisees and trainees see clinical decision making as an instance of problem-solving by reviewing the articles described above (Geiger et al., 2012; LeBlanc et al., 2016) with the trainee, explaining the use of the table in Step 3 of problem-solving.

Finally, the supervisor should encourage the supervisee to view this problem-solving process as a safety net that will help them become more confident and competent at problem-solving. In addition, step 5 of the model creates the opportunity to talk about mistakes as valuable learning experiences that enhance future problem-solving (i.e., we learn what not to do as well as what to do). The supervisor might describe an instance when a strategy that they felt certain would work failed and what the next steps were. The supervisor must create an environment that encourages and reinforces honesty about mistakes and problems that have been detected.

Reflection	Action

✓ Think about a time when you faced a problem and identified a successful solution:
  ◦ Did you use any of the five steps of the structured process?
  ◦ What was the outcome?
 	
✓ Think about some of the common problems you have encountered in clinical practice and supervision and if your colleagues have shared encountering similar issues.
 	
✓ Use Appendix B of LeBlanc, Sellers et al., (2020) to reflect on any potential difficulties you might have with problem-solving.
	✓ Review the entire Ethics Code for Behavior Analysts (BACB, 2020) for examples of ethical problem-solving.
	
	✓ Complete Appendix A of Chapter 7 LeBlanc, Sellers et al. (2020) – Problem Solving Worksheet with a variety of problems.
	
	✓ Use a clinical decision-making model to collaboratively select a measurement system or function-based treatment for problem behavior.
	
	✓ Identify a person who remains calm throughout problem-solving and interview them about their problem-solving approach.

Resources

1. Kieta, A.R., Cihon, T.M. & Abdel-Jalil, A. (2019). Problem-solving from a behavioral perspective: Implications for behavior analysts and educators. *Journal of Behavioral Education, 28,* 275–300 (2019).

2. LeBlanc, L. A., (2020). *Nobody's perfect.* Retrieved on April 3, 2020, from https://www.aubreydaniels.com/media-center/nobodys-perfect

3. LeBlanc, L. A., Sellers, T. P., & Alai, S. (2020). *Building and sustaining meaningful and effective relationships as a supervisor and mentor.* Sloan Publishing. Chapter 7.

4. Robbins, J. K. (2011). Problem-solving, reasoning, and analytical thinking in a classroom environment. *The Behavior Analyst Today, 12*(1), 40–47.

5. Skinner, B. F. (1984). An operant analysis of problem-solving. *Behavioral and Brain Sciences, 7*(4), 583–591.

Public Speaking and Professional Presentations

What These Are

For the purposes of practicing behavior analysts, we will adopt the meaning of *public speaking* offered by Friman (2014): anytime speaking in front of an audience. Certainly, presenting at a conference is public speaking, but so is presenting at an Individual Education Plan meeting, conducting a training, and leading a meeting (Heinicke et al., in press). Public speaking involves disseminating information about the profession, the science, or clinical practice for the purposes of increasing understanding, demonstrating how to do something, or solving a shared problem. *Professional presentation* is a component of public speaking that involves the sharing of information or data, usually visually, in the form of reports, slides, graphs, or videos.

Why They Are Important

Effective public speaking and presenting skills are the primary ways to disseminate information and train skills. The ability to clearly communicate through vocal, verbal behavior and the presentation of well-organized visual material is critical to the success of an independent clinical practitioner and supervisor. These skills can result in increased confidence in and access to services and can facilitate collaboration, problem-solving, and the acquisition of skills targeted in training. These skills are critical when interacting with caregivers, other professionals, funding sources, and trainees and colleagues. On the other hand, poor public speaking and presenting skills can result in distrust, misunderstanding, and ineffective training (Heinicke et al., in press). Some common issues with public speaking include anxiety, presence of disfluencies (i.e., responses produced by the speaker that interrupt the flow of their vocal behavior), poor audience control (e.g., failing to effectively match one's vocal, verbal behavior to their listener), overreliance on a script, and avoiding public speaking. (Heinicke et al., in press). Common problems with presenting are related to the amount, (too much or not enough), organization or flow, and focus (too in-depth or too surface) of the information being shared. Another issue related to presenting information is related to the quality of the visual material (e.g., overly complicated or blurry diagrams and graphs, slides with too much text). All these issues can result in the audience disengaging from the content, as well as frustration and misunderstanding on the part of the audience and the speaker.

Assessing These Skills

Assessing skills related to public speaking and presenting may be difficult for a few reasons. If individuals are very nervous, they may avoid accepting opportunities to speak publicly and supervisors may be reluctant to provide these opportunities, or they may simply not be available. One way to begin to assess these skills is to ask the individual how they feel about public speaking and what they perceive their skills to be. Attending to how individuals perform in individual, small, and large group meetings can also provide some measure of these skills. For example, if they rarely participate and when they do, they struggle to communicate their thoughts or questions in an organized manner, that may be an indicator that they will need some additional instruction and support to develop the related skills. Another option is to assign small, low-stakes practice presentations and evaluate things such as presence of disfluencies, rate of speech and breathing, tone of voice, general affect, organization of the material, and use of visuals. Heinicke et al., (in press) provide a form in the appendices for evaluating public speaking that could be used to assess or self-assess public-speaking skills.

The indicators below will be most relevant to new BCBAs. These indicators may be relevant to supervisees who have roles that include the expectation to engage in public speaking and presenting (e.g., staff training, caregiver training, interviewing applicants). For trainees, these indicators may be helpful as they advance through their experience hours and get closer to independent practice.

Skill Level	New BCBA	Supervisees/Trainees
Not yet acquired	✓ Avoidance or refusal to engage in public speaking or presenting. ✓ Infrequently or never able to clearly communicate intended information through public speaking or presenting. ✓ Unable to engage in public speaking and presenting to a wide range of audiences (e.g., caregivers, supervisees and trainees, peers, other professionals) and for a variety of purposes (dissemination, sharing information, training). ✓ Infrequently or never identifies what visual supports may be helpful to present information. ✓ Infrequently or never produces an outline of material in an organized manner. ✓ Infrequently or never produces adequate or generally organized visual supports for a presentation.	✓ Low or no participation in team meetings or staff training. ✓ Infrequently or never expresses questions or comments in a succinct and organized manner. ✓ Infrequently or never clearly communicates across a variety of audiences and topics. ✓ Infrequently or never identifies what visual supports may be helpful to present information. ✓ Infrequently or never outlines material in an organized manner.

Skill Level	New BCBA	Supervisees/Trainees
Developing	✓ Hesitant acceptance to engage in formal public speaking or presenting but able to request assistance. ✓ Frequently communicates some information through public speaking or presenting, likely relying on scripts or other prompts with success. ✓ Able to engage in public speaking and presenting to a few different audiences (e.g., caregivers, supervisees and trainees, peers, other professionals) and for a few different purposes (dissemination, sharing information, training). ✓ Frequently identifies some visual supports that may be helpful to present information. ✓ Frequently outlines material in an organized manner. ✓ Frequently produces adequate or well-organized visual supports for a presentation.	✓ Consistent, active participation in team meetings or staff training. ✓ Frequently expresses questions or comments in a succinct and organized manner. ✓ Frequently communicates across a few audiences and topics with success. ✓ Frequently identifies some visual supports that may be helpful to present information. ✓ Frequently outlines material in a somewhat organized manner.

Teaching These Skills

As with many skills, public speaking and presenting skills can be expressly taught with BST. Depending on an individual's skill level, it may be important to break the task of public speaking and presenting into component skills, or identify specific barriers, and focus on those. For example, if an individual engages in high levels of disfluencies or a very slow rate of speech, it may be worth focusing on reducing disfluencies or increasing rate of speech before focusing on creating and delivering a public presentation. Some strategies to consider include frequent practice opportunities in small and large group settings, using visual and auditory cues to influence rates of speech and frequency of disfluencies, and identifying a core message with which the audience can connect. For presenting skills, some strategies include making an outline of the content, selecting visuals that can help the audience connect with the material, and minimizing the amount of text on slides. Another strategy is to have individuals give short presentations on familiar topics to their peers and provide feedback to one another using a structured checklist. Finally, if individuals use PowerPoint, consider teaching them to use the design tools, particularly the "design ideas" feature for an individual slide.

Friman offers 15 steps to increasing one's public speaking skills in his 2014 article. The article by Heinicke and colleagues (in press) provides specific strategies for teaching and improving public speaking and presentation skills that can be used to support teaching these skills. The authors also include a sample public feedback speaking form for evaluating and gathering feedback and a public speaking preparation checklist. Most importantly, for supervisors and mentors, they provide specific considerations and ideas across the BST components of describing, modeling, and practicing with feedback (Appendix C: Considerations for Supervisors/Mentors).

Reflection	Action
✓ Think about the physical and covert responses you have when thinking about or engaging in public speaking and presenting. ✓ Think about activities that you can engage in to reduce anxiety or stress related to public speaking and presenting (e.g., relaxation activities, practicing, co-presenting). ✓ Think about why being an effective public speaker is important.	✓ Identify and watch individuals who are excellent public speakers and presenters, paying close attention to what they do that is effective. ✓ Use self-management to set goals for yourself (e.g., identify a specific number of questions to ask or contributions to make in a meeting, decide that you will accept the next opportunity to engage in public speaking, ask for an opportunity). ✓ Create an opportunity to practice with peers, friends, or family. ✓ Play games that require some form of public speaking or presenting (e.g., Pictionary, Telegraphs, Charades). ✓ Take a workshop, course, or join a group that focuses on public speaking (e.g., Toastmasters, an improvisation class).

Resources

1. Friman, P. C. (2014). Behavior analysts to the front! A 15-step tutorial on public speaking. *The Behavior Analyst, 37,* 109–118. https://doi.org/10.1007/s40614-014-0009-y

2. Heinicke, M. R., Juanico, J. F., Valentino, A. L., & Sellers, T. P. (in press). Improving behavior analysts' public speaking: Recommendations from expert interviews. *Behavior Analysis in Practice.*

3. Effective Presentations Inc. (2019). *Public speaking training workshops, classes and coaching.* https://www.effectivepresentations.com/public/public-speaking-training/

4. Glassman, L. H., Forman, E. M., Herbert, J. D., Bradley, L. E., Foster, E. E., Izzetoglu, M., & Rocco, A. C. (2016). The effects of a brief acceptance-based behavioral treatment versus traditional cognitive-behavioral treatment for public-speaking anxiety: An exploratory trial examining differential effects on performance and neurophysiology. *Behavior Modification, 40,* 748–776. https://doi.org/10.1177/0145445516629939

5. Laborda, M. A., Schofield, C. A., Johnson, E. M., Schubert, J. R., George-Denn, D., Coles, M. E., & Miller, R. R. (2016). The extinction and return of fear of public speaking. *Behavior Modification, 40,* 901–921. https://doi.org/10.1177/0145445516645766

6. Mancuso, C., & Miltenberger, R. G. (2016). Using habit reversal to decrease filled pauses in public speaking. *Journal of Applied Behavior Analysis, 49,* 1–5. https://doi.org/10.1002/jaba.267

7. Mladenka, J. D., Sawyer, C. R., & Behnke, R. R. (1998). Anxiety sensitivity and speech trait anxiety as predictors of state anxiety during public speaking. *Communication Quarterly, 46,* 417–429. https://doi.org/10.1080/01463379809370112

8. Montes, C. C., Heinicke, M. R., & Geierman, D. M. (2019). Awareness training reduces college students' speech disfluencies in public speaking. *Journal of Applied Behavior Analysis, 52,* 746–755. https://doi.org/10.1002/jaba.569

9. North, M. (2019). *10 tips for improving your public speaking skills.* Harvard Extension School Professional Development Blog. https://professional.dce.harvard.edu/blog/10-tips-for-improving-your-public-speaking-skills/

10. O'Hair, D., Rubenstein, H., & Stewart, R. (2015). *A pocket guide to public speaking.* Bedford/St. Martin's.

11. Spieler, C., & Miltenberger, R. (2017). Using awareness training to decrease nervous habits during public speaking. *Journal of Applied Behavior Analysis, 50,* 38–47. https://doi.org/10.1002/jaba.362

12. Toastmasters. (2019). *All about toastmasters.* https://www.toastmasters.org/about/all-about-toastmasters/

13. Valentino, A. L., LeBlanc, L. A., & Sellers, T. P. (2016). The benefits of group supervision and a recommended structure for implementation. *Behavior Analysis in Practice, 9,* 320–328. https://doi.org/10.1007/s40617-016-0138-8

Scope Of Competence

What This Is

Let's start by first describing *scope of practice*. Brodhead et al. (2018) note that scope of practice is used to indicate the constellation of activities appropriate for individuals in a profession to practice based on a certification, credential, or license. *Scope of competence* generally refers to a professional's ability to consistently perform a skill or task effectively and accurately, typically meeting some predetermined expectation or criterion. In the Ethics Code for Behavior Analysts, *scope of competence* is defined as "The professional activities a behavior analyst can consistently perform with proficiency." (BACB, 2020, p. 8). In summary, *scope of practice* is defined for the profession by oversight organizations (e.g., BACB, licensure boards), whereas scope of competence is measured at the individual professional level (e.g., BCBA, BCaBA, RBT, trainee).

Why This Is Important

It is critical for each BCBA to understand their own scope of competence at a given point in their career, and to continually evaluate it, to maximize benefits and avoid causing harm. The quality of ABA services and outcomes are directly dependent on the skill level of the service providers. Inadequate service delivery, whether clinical services or supervision and training, has serious risks for the recipients. Low-quality clinical services can result in lost time due to delayed progress with acquisition or behavior reduction interventions, worsening of behavior of concern, and risk of physical and emotional harm to consumers. Poor training and supervision can result in skill deficits for trainees and supervisees,

as well as all the previously listed risks for consumers. ABA services are evidence-based and driven by existing and ever-progressing research. Therefore, it is incumbent on BCBAs to continually evaluate, maintain, and adjust their skills to remain in line with current practice recommendations. Furthermore, BCBAs providing supervision to supervisees and trainees must also teach them how to evaluate their scope of competence.

Assessing This Skill

The ability to accurately describe and evaluate one's own scope of competence can be assessed by having discussions about what scope of competence is and what factors should be considered when evaluating one's scope of competence. The primary function of being able to fully understand one's own scope of competence is to ensure that one practices only within this scope, as practicing outside it invites risk of harm. Therefore, another activity to assist in assessing this skill is to present a variety of case examples with a wide range of settings, populations, presenting needs, and assessment and intervention technologies and asking the individual if they feel competent to independently provide services for the case example. If they indicate that they do, ask them to describe the training and experience they have that makes them competent. If they indicate that they are not competent, ask them to list why and what they would do if they wanted to expand their scope of competence. Alligood and Gravina (2021) and LeBlanc et al. (2012) provide specific strategies for expanding one's area of practice and scope of competence.

Use the indicators in the table below to assess if an individual has yet to begin acquiring skills related to evaluating their scope of competence, or if the skills are emerging.

Skill Level	New BCBA	Supervisees/Trainees
Not yet acquired	✓ Unable to describe scope of competence, why it is important, and the associate risks of failing to practice with one's scope of competence. ✓ Unable to describe the factors to consider when evaluating one's scope of competence. ✓ Infrequently or never identifies resources related to scope of competence. ✓ Indicating that they can or should be able to engage in certain tasks for which they do not have proper training. ✓ Engaging in practices and activities without the proper training. ✓ Delegating practices and tasks to others who lack proper training.	✓ Unable to describe scope of competence, why it is important, and the associate risks of failing to practice with one's scope of competence. ✓ Infrequently or never identifies resources related to scope of competence. ✓ Indicating that they can or should be able to engage in certain tasks for which they do not have proper training. ✓ Engaging in practices and activities without the proper training, particularly without asking a supervisor.
Developing	✓ Able to provide a sufficient description of scope of competence, but might not have full understanding of the associated importance or risks. ✓ Frequently identifies resources (e.g., ethics standards, articles). ✓ Able to describe some of the factors to consider when evaluating. ✓ Able to accurately identify some practices within and outside of their own and other's scope of competence. ✓ Appropriately seeking out guidance related to scope of competence. ✓ Appropriately delegating some practices and tasks to others. ✓ Appropriately withholding some tasks from others.	✓ Able to provide an emerging or accurate description of scope of competence. ✓ Frequently identifies related ethics standards. ✓ Able to accurately describe some tasks within and outside of their scope of competence. ✓ Appropriately seeking support from supervisor when concerned about practicing outside of scope of competence.

Teaching This Skill

In taking a BST approach to teaching the skill of evaluating one's scope of competence should include a discussion of the skill, modeling the skill, and rehearsing the skill with feedback until mastery. When describing the skill, be sure to include the following points:

1. BACB ethics standards,
2. the benefits,
3. the risks, and
4. the idea that this is a continual practice throughout one's career.

You can model the skill throughout your supervisory relationship and in clinical settings by describing a) how and when you self-assess; and b) your scope of competence in relation to accepting or not accepting clients, supervisees, and trainees. The rehearsal component should include a variety of role-plays with case scenarios to which individual can indicate a) if they have the relevant competence, b) why or why not, c) the risks of accepting the client if the needs are outside of their scope, and d) actions they might take if the clients' needs were outside their scope (e.g., refer out, co-treat, gain the skills via training or consultation).

Use the strategies on the following page to build your own skills, discussing them with your CS regularly. Set goals for yourself, track progress, and share with your CS. Use the strategies on the following page to build the skills of your supervisees or trainees. Add content to their competency-based roadmap, agendas, and observation checklists. Use the results of your scope of competency self-assessment activities to begin to identify areas for growth and expansion and discuss with your CS.

Use the reflection activities together with your CS (for you), or trainees (for them), or by yourself to support your skills in evaluating and identifying your scope of competence. Similarly, the actions can be used together with your CS to facilitate your skills, by you with your trainees to develop their skills, or on your own to independently work on your own skills.

Reflection	Action
✓ Reflect on the definition of scope of competence, its importance, and risks.	✓ Make a list of the following variables relative to your work experience: populations worked with, settings worked in, assessment and intervention procedures designed and completed, clinical practices engaged in (e.g., report writing, interviewing), supervising and training, performance monitoring and management.
✓ Reflect on what thoughts and feelings come up around the topic of scope of competence.	
✓ Reflect on your training contexts and the degree to which you received high-quality training and supervision.	✓ Now go back and add in the following for each of the above variables: observed, assisted, trained to predetermined competency, completed independently, trained others.
✓ Reflect on whether you were trained to competency.	
✓ Reflect on the skills and activities you regularly engage in, and those with which you might be rusty.	✓ For any variables you indicated independent completion and/or trained others write the number of consecutive years (e.g., working with a given population, implementing a given intervention technology) and number of months/years since (if applicable).
✓ Reflect on whether anyone has ever talked to you about their scope of competence, and if so:	
◦ What was the context (e.g., indicating something was within or outside their scope of competence)?	✓ Review the related standards in the Ethics Code for Behavior Analysts and the RBT Ethics Code.
◦ What did they say?	✓ Read articles and discuss.
◦ How did the conversation make you feel?	✓ Complete the self-assessment in Brodhead et al. (2018).
✓ Reflect on whether anyone has expressly trained you how to evaluate scope of competence.	✓ Calendar time to engage in regular (e.g., quarterly) self-evaluation of your scope of competence until it becomes fluent.
✓ Reflect on whether you can recall an instance where you think you or someone else may have acted outside of your or their scope of competence, the outcome, and if you would do anything differently now.	

Resources

1. Alligood, C. A., & Gravina, N. E. (2021). Branching out: Finding success in new areas of practice. *Behavior Analysis in Practice, 14*(1), 283-289.

2. Briggs, A. M., & Mitteer, D. R. (2021). Updated strategies for making regular contact with the scholarly literature. *Behavior Analysis in Practice*, 1-12.

3. Brodhead, M. T., Quigley, S. P., & Wilczynski, S. M. (2018). A call for discussion about scope of competence in behavior analysis. *Behavior Analysis in Practice, 11*(4), 424-435.

4. Carr, J. E., & Briggs, A. M. (2010). Strategies for making regular contact with the scholarly literature. *Behavior Analysis in Practice, 3*(2), 13-18.

5. LeBlanc, L. A., Heinicke, M. R., & Baker, J. C. (2012). Expanding the consumer base for behavior-analytic services: Meeting the needs of consumers in the 21st century. *Behavior Analysis in Practice, 5*(1), 4-14.

6. LeBlanc, L. A., Sellers, T. P., & Ala'i, S. (2020). *Building and sustaining meaningful and effective relationships as a supervisor and mentor*. Sloan Publishing.

Self-Care

What This Is

Figley (2002) described *self-care* as actively engaging practices or behavior focused on facilitating quality of life and managing work-life balance. Self-care typically involves engaging in self-monitoring to assess one's behavior and needs and self-management to enact plans for improvement of self-care practices. Self-care practices must be individualized, and they are specifically tied to one's history, intersecting cultural identity, and current context. However, self-care practices typically involve evaluating and engaging in behaviors in the following areas: physical health, emotional/psychological health, spiritual practices, personal and social behavior, and professional and workplace behavior.

Why This Is Important

The work of a clinician is exciting and valuable. At the same time, it can be stressful and produce burnout (Plantiveau et al., 2018). Burnout can produce diminished enjoyment of an individual's work and can invite drifting from high-quality practices resulting in less-optimal outcomes for, and possible harm to clients, caregivers, supervisees, and trainees. Burnout may impact some individuals so severely that they choose to leave the profession. Actively self-assessing and managing self-care needs and practices can increase an individual's ability to manage stress and work-life balance and can facilitate a reinforcing and sustained career in behavior analysis.

Assessing This Skill

Self-care skills can be assessed in a number of ways. Supervisors, managers, and mentors should continually engage in careful observation of individuals to detect indicators of stress (e.g., fatigue, changes in affect and quality of work, statements of being overwhelmed). Regular check-ins during meetings provide the perfect opportunity to ask questions and have meaningful discussions around stress levels, work-life balance, and self-care activities. Chapters 7, 8, 9, 10, and 11 in the LeBlanc, Sellers et al. (2020) book provide recommendations and resources for assessing repertoires that are often related to, or provide an indication of, increased stress (e.g., organization and time management, issues in the supervisory relationship). One only needs to enter the words *self-care assessment* or *assessing stress* into a search engine to find a number of helpful tools for assessing self-care and levels of stress that can be used as self-assessments or to facilitate discussions about assessing an individual's stress levels and self-care practices. For example, the Boston School of Social Work Center for Innovation in Social Work & Health provides free online access to the *Self-Assessment Tool: Self-Care*, a PDF that provides structured self-rating items across the areas of physical, psychological, emotional, spiritual, and workplace/professional self-care (Boston School of Social Work, n.d.).

Skill Level	New BCBA	Supervisees/Trainees
Not yet acquired	✓ Frequent statements related to feeling unable to manage workload or work-life balance. ✓ Frequent statements that work is not reinforcing or fun, ✓ Frequent disruptions to work; activities seemingly related to stress (e.g., frequent cancellations and missed deadlines). ✓ Activity level is frequent barrier to completing tasks (e.g., low or high energy results in poor follow-through). ✓ Frequent emotional responding in a variety of contexts (e.g., crying, snapping at people). ✓ Rarely or never says no to opportunities or tasks. ✓ Rarely or never asks for support.	✓ Same
Developing	✓ Some statements indicating identification they need to take action to manage workload or work-life balance. ✓ Scheduling planned time off. ✓ Moderate to infrequent disruptions to work activities and tacting when they are relating difficulty managing workload, stress, or work-life balance. ✓ Some active management of activity level (e.g., engaging strategies to elevate activity level or manage distractions). ✓ Moderate to infrequent emotional responding; when emotional responding occurs strategies to mediate are implemented; strategies are implemented to minimize emotional responding (e.g., scripts and practice for difficult conversation, breathing activities).	✓ Same

Teaching This Skill

Supervisors should focus on teaching supervisees and trainees how to engage in frequent self-assessment and self-reflection related to self-care and stress management, as well as how to create and manage a plan for self-care. This is likely best accomplished through discussion and practice; however, it is critical to follow the lead of the individual in these endeavors. Some individuals may feel comfortable discussing the topics and exploring tools but may not feel comfortable completing the self-assessments or self-care planning collaboratively with their supervisor. Therefore, emphasis should be placed on discussion, reviewing resources and tools, frequent check-ins, and the offer to practice or support the individual in the development of a self-care plan, goals, and activities. Regardless of the degree of collaboration, highlighting the use of self-monitoring, self-reflection, and self-management practices to support self-care will be critical. LeBlanc, Sellers et al. (2020) provide descriptions of these practices and resources to support them in chapters 2, 3, 4, and 6, and offer additional guidance in skills-specific chapters related to subjects such as problem-solving and organization and time management. They also include strategies for taking an active approach to planning for a sustained and rewarding career in chapter 12. Fiebig et al. (2020) describe strategies and resources for engaging in self-care activities, including activities to identify and clarify values that can support engaging in self-care practices.

Reflection	Action
✓ Spend some time thinking about your feelings and private events related to your typical work and life activities. ✓ Think about work and life activities that bring you joy and those that cause frustration or discomfort and reflect on possible barriers (e.g., lack of resources or skills). ✓ Think about how you feel and behave when your work or life stressors are well managed and when they are not well managed; how you think others are impacted in each situation.	✓ Write down words that describe how you feel about your work and life (e.g., energized, exhausted, frustrated). ✓ Complete a self-care, self-compassion, or compassion-fatigue self-assessment. ✓ Make a recipe that describes the ingredients needed for you to perform at your best in work and life activities (e.g., minimal number of hours of sleep or exercise, minimal frequency engaging in hobbies, leisure, or social activities, minimal support needed from managers or supervisors, necessary resources). ✓ Create a self-management plan focusing on goals for your self-care.

Resources

1. Boston School of Social Work Center for Innovation in Social Work & Health (n.d.). *Self- assessment tool: Self-Care.* https://www.ucebt.com/images/pdfs-doc/SelfAssessmentToolSelfCare-PeerRole-Peer_Training.pdf

2. Fiebig, J. H., Gould, E. R., Ming, S., & Watson, R. A. (2020). An invitation to act on the value of self-care: Being a whole person in all that you do. *Behavior Analysis in Practice*, 1-9.

3. Figley, C. R. (2002). Compassion fatigue: Psychotherapists' chronic lack of self-care. *Journal of Clinical Psychology, 58*(11), 1433-1441.

4. LeBlanc, L. A., Sellers, T. P., & Ala'i, S. (2020). *Building and sustaining meaningful and effective relationships as a supervisor and mentor*, Chapter 5. Sloan Publishing.

5. Plantiveau, C., Dounavi, K., & Virués-Ortega, J. (2018). High levels of burnout among early career board-certified behavior analysts with low collegial support in the work environment. *European Journal of Behavior Analysis, 19*(2), 195-207.

Teaching Effectively Using Behavioral Skills Training (BST)

What This Is

Parsons et al. (2012) describe this competency-based training method as including the six following steps:

1. providing a description of the skill (i.e., verbal instruction)
2. giving a written/visual description of the skill (i.e., written instruction including job aids)
3. demonstrating the skill (i.e., modeling),
4. providing practice opportunities (i.e., rehearsal)
5. providing feedback on the performance during rehearsal
6. repeating those 5 steps until the desired performance criterion is reached

Miltenberger (2015) describes BST as including four main components:

1. instructions
2. modeling
3. rehearsal
4. feedback until a performance criterion is reached

Regardless of whether you break BST into 4 or 6 steps, this type of training places importance on direct performance opportunities and continuation of training until new skills are repeatedly demonstrated through accurate performance. Without rehearsal and feedback opportunities, most people will be unable to consistently perform at a high level after training is completed (i.e., skill maintenance).

Instructions. This step involves providing a clear description of the skill with detail about each component and why it is important. The information should be presented in manageable chunks and the rationales should focus on the benefits of implementing the skill correctly, the risks of error, and any nuances associated with each skill. The vocal and written instructions should be clear and concise. They may include a job aid, which is a permanently available, concisely written description of a task in the form of a checklist, summary sheet, flowchart, or screen capture (LeBlanc, Sellers et al., 2020). This component is often combined or alternated with the next component—modeling.

Modeling. Modeling involves demonstration of the target skill and can take the form of a live demonstration or video model. If the demonstration is live, it should be carefully scripted in advance. The models should include multiple exemplars of correct implementation of the skill. Video models may also allow demonstration of the skill with multiple people and in multiple contexts. The demonstration should begin with a simple version of the skill with increased complexity in later demonstrations. In addition, the supervisor may alternate providing instructions and modeling components if a skill is complicated and involves multiple steps (i.e., instructions and modeling for step 1, instructions and modeling for step 2, instructions and modeling for step 3, rehearsal of steps 1-3).

Rehearsal. The rehearsal component involves actively practicing the target skill in a role-play or natural context. The practice activities should proceed from simple to more complex with introduction of distractors and disruptors (e.g., prompting, collecting data, addressing problem behavior) before the skill is considered mastered. The new skills may initially be rehearsed at a much slower pace and with extensive use of the job aids to ensure that the person being trained has an opportunity to perform correctly and encounter reinforcement. This step is often interspersed with the following step: feedback. That is, during or after each practice opportunity, the trainer typically provides supportive and corrective feedback followed by another opportunity to practice the skill.

Feedback. *Feedback* refers to providing information about some specific aspect of a performance in comparison to some criterion. Feedback is one of the most powerful tools we have for shaping and maintaining a supervisee's performance. In the context of initial training, it is important to provide feedback about each aspect of the performance in a way that corresponds to the prior instruction. That is, if you described four components of the skill, you should provide feedback on the rehearsal performance for each of those four components. If three were performed accurately, praise the success for each of these as well as pointing out errors on the other component. Generally, feedback is provided immediately during initial training trials and the delay is gradually increased by the end of training when performance is highly accurate. See the Skill Section on Feedback for additional detail about the specific delivery of feedback.

Repeated Practice Until Competent. The steps and components outlined above are subject to evaluation of their effectiveness. Although this procedure has a strong evidence base to support its effectiveness in general, the trainer should be evaluating the effects of their unique implementation of BST on the performance of the person they are training. Throughout practice and feedback, there should be data collected on the accuracy of the skill. That performance should be evaluated against a success criterion, exactly as we would do when teaching a client a new skill. The criterion will vary based on the complexity and importance of the skill, but the criterion should specify a minimum acceptable level of accuracy (e.g., 90% accuracy) and stability (e.g., across two practice sessions) for performance. Training should not be considered complete until that success criterion has been reached.

Why This Is Important

Both the Ethics Code for Behavior Analysts (BACB, 2020) and the Supervisor Training Curriculum Outline 2.0 (BACB, 2018) specify that behavior analysts should implement effective training. Behavioral Skills Training (BST) is an effective and evidence-based training strategy (Parsons et al., 2012; Miltenberger, 2015) that has been investigated across a wide range of target skills. This approach stands in stark contrast to traditional classroom instruction where instructions are provided for a pre-determined amount of time but there is no demonstration that the skill has been acquired. Though it is more effortful than the traditional model, it is also more effective. It is important to include all components of BST because without rehearsal and feedback opportunities, most people will be unable to consistently perform at a high level after training is completed (i.e., skill maintenance).

Assessing These Skills

These skills can be assessed through permanent product, role-play, and in vivo performance. For example, trainees could submit permanent products such as a PowerPoint presentation for the instructions, a job aid, or a data sheet to use during rehearsal. For role-playing delivery of the instructions and implementation or rehearsal and feedback, group supervision might provide an opportunity for trainees to serve as the trainer in some role-plays and as the learner in other role-plays. The assignment could focus on a particular component (e.g., creating a job aid, creating a video model) but it is important to assess the ability to implement all components of BST eventually.

Skill Level	New BCBA	Supervisees/Trainees
Not yet acquired	✓ Instructions may be overly complex or lack detail. ✓ No rationale is given, or the rationale does not adequately convey the importance of accuracy and the risk of error. ✓ Trainee infrequently or never creates an effective job aid. ✓ Models do not capture the critical components of the skill or do not illustrate multiple exemplars. ✓ Training is considered complete without demonstration of accurate performance. ✓ Feedback is non-specific or overly focused on errors. ✓ No success criterion is used.	✓ Same
Developing	✓ Instructions are brief and concise. ✓ The rationale accurately and clearly conveys the importance of the skill and correct performance. ✓ Job aids contain crisp visuals that aid performance. ✓ Multiple models are used during training. ✓ Models illustrate the critical components of the skill. ✓ Rehearsal and feedback are repeated until a success criterion is met. ✓ Feedback focuses on accurate performance as well as errors. ✓ Feedback is delivered in an acceptable and compassionate manner.	✓ Same

Teaching These Skills

These skills are foundational to effective supervision and should be covered in academic coursework related to supervision and personnel management. However, academic coursework alone is unlikely to produce a robust repertoire for training others. It is important to review the content from coursework as a form of instruction, model the use of BST as you teach the trainee various other skills (e.g., active listening, ethical decision making), and allow opportunities to practice the component skills until mastery. That is, use BST to teach your trainees how to use BST.

Reflection	Action
✓ Think about a prior teacher, supervisor, coach, or trainer who was very effective at teaching you something. Did they use any of the components of BST? ✓ Think about a prior teacher, supervisor, coach, or trainer who was not effective at teaching you something. Which of the components of BST were missing in their instruction?	✓ Review the relevant standards (4.06, 4.08, and 4.10) from the Ethics Code for Behavior Analysts (BACB, 2020). ✓ Identify a skill that you think would be easy to teach using BST and create the materials. ✓ Identify a skill that you think would be hard to teach using BST and describe what would be hard about it.

Resources

1. LeBlanc, L. A., Sellers, T. P., & Ala'i, S. (2020). *Building and sustaining meaningful and effective relationships as a supervisor and mentor*, Chapter 5. Sloan Publishing.

2. Miltenberger, R. G. (2015). *Behavior modification: Principles and procedures* (6th Edition). Cengage.

3. Parsons, M. B., Rollyson, J. H., & Reid, D. H. (2012). Evidence-based staff training. *Behavior Analysis in Practice, 5*, 2–11. doi: 10.1007/BF03391819

References

Allen, D. A. (2015). *Getting things done: The art of stress-free productivity*(Revised). Penguin Publishing.

Allen, D. A., & Hall, B. (2019). *The getting things done workbook: 10 moves to stress-free productivity*. Platkus.

Alligood, C. A., & Gravina, N. E. (2021). Branching out: Finding success in new areas of practice. *Behavior Analysis in Practice, 14*(1), 283-289.

Axe, J. B., Phelan, S. H., & Irwin, C. L. (2019). Empirical evaluations of Skinner's problem-solving analysis. *The Analysis of Verbal Behavior, 35*(1), 39–56. doi. org/10.1007/s40616-018-0103-4.

Bailey, J., & Burch, M. (2010). *25 essential skills & strategies for the professional behavior analyst*. Routledge.

Bandura, A. B. (1997). *Self-efficacy: The exercise of control*. W. H. Freeman.

Behavior Analyst Certification Board. (2017). BCBA task list (5th ed.). Littleton, CO: Author.

Behavior Analyst Certification Board. (2018). *Supervision training curriculum outline (2.0)* Littleton, CO: Author.

Behavior Analyst Certification Board. (2020). *Ethics code for behavior analysts*. Littleton, CO: Author.

Behavior Analyst Certification Board. (August, 2021a). *Final experience verification form: Individual supervisor*. https://www.bacb. com/wp-content/uploads/2020/05/ BACB-Final Experience-Verification-Form-Individual_210825.pdf

Behavior Analyst Certification Board. (August, 2021b). *Monthly fieldwork verification form individual supervisor 2022 fieldwork requirements*. https://www.bacb.com/ wpcontent/uploads/2020/06/BACB-Monthly-Fieldwork-Verification-Form-Individual_2021_08_25.pdf

Behavior Analyst Certification Board. (May, 2021a). *BCBA® board certified behavior analyst® handbook*. https://www.bacb. com/wp content/uploads/2020/11/ BCBAHandbook_210513.pdf

Behavior Analyst Certification Board. (May, 2021b). *Consulting supervisor requirements for new BCBAs supervising fieldwork training curriculum outline*. https://www.bacb. com/wp-content/uploads/2020/11/ Consultation-Supervisor-Requirements-and-Documentation_210528.pdf

Behavior Analyst Certification Board. (September, 2021). *BCBA® 2022 eligibility requirements*. https://www.bacb.com/wp-content/uploads/2021/09/BCBA-2022Eli gibilityRequirements_210915-2.pdf

Behavior Analyst Certification Board. (n.d.a). *BACB certificant data*. Retrieved 2021, December 05 from https://www.bacb. com/bacb-certificant-data/

Behavior Analyst Certification Board. (n.d.b). *Sample supervision contract for BCBA/ BCaBA Trainees*. Retrieved 2021, December 05 from https://www.bacb.com/ search/?q=Sample%20Supervision%20 Contract%20

Boston School of Social Work Center for Innovation in Social Work & Health (n.d.). *Self-assessment tool: Self-care*. https:// www.ucebt.com/images/pdfs-doc/ SelfAssessmentToolSelfCare-PeerRole-Peer_Training.pdf\

Brodhead, M. T., Quigley, S. P., & Wilczynski, S. M. (2018). A call for discussion about scope of competence in behavior analysis. *Behavior Analysis in Practice, 11*(4), 424-435.

Carr, J. E., Wilder, D. A., Majdalany, L., Mathisen, D., & Strain, L. A. (2013). An assessment-based solution to a human-service employee performance problem. *Behavior Analysis in Practice, 6*, 16–32.

Chase, J. A., Houmanfar, R., Hayes, S. C., Ward, T. A., Vilardaga, J. P., & Follette, V. (2013). Values are not just goals: Online ACT-based values training adds to goal setting in improving undergraduate college student performance. *Journal of Contextual Behavioral Science, 2*(3-4), 79-84.

Cooper, J. O., Heron, T. E., & Heward, W. L. (2020). *Applied behavior analysis.* Pearson.

Donahoe, J. W., & Palmer, D. C. (2004). *Learning and complex behavior.* Boston: Allyn & Bacon.

Ervin, N. E. (2008). Caseload management skills for improved efficiency. *The Journal of Continuing Education in Nursing, 39*(3), 127–132.

Fiebig, J. H., Gould, E. R., Ming, S., & Watson, R. A. (2020). An invitation to act on the value of self-care: Being a whole person in all that you do. *Behavior Analysis in Practice,* 1-9.

Figley, C. R. (2002). Compassion fatigue: Psychotherapists' chronic lack of self-care. *Journal of Clinical Psychology, 58*(11), 1433-1441.

Friman, P. C. (2014). Behavior analysts to the front! A 15-step tutorial on public speaking. *The Behavior Analyst, 37*, 109–118. https://doi.org/ 10.1007/s40614-014-0009-y.

Garza, K. L., McGee, H. M., Schenk, Y. A., & Wiskirchen, R. R. (2018). Some tools for carrying out a proposed process for supervising experience hours for aspiring Board-Certified Behavior Analysts®. *Behavior Analysis in Practice, 11*, 62–70.

Geiger, K. A., Carr, J. E., & LeBlanc, L. A. (2010). Function-based treatments for escape-maintained problem behavior: A treatment selection model for practicing behavior analysts. *Behavior Analysis in Practice, 3*, 22–32.

Gravina, N., Villacorta, J., Albert, K., Clark, R., Curry, S., & Wilder, D. (2018). A literature review of organizational behavior management interventions in human service settings from 1990 to 2016. *Journal of Organizational Behavior Management, 38*(23), 191–224. doi:10.1080/01608061.201 8.1454872

Grow, L. L., Carr, J. E., & LeBlanc, L. A. (2009). Treatments for attention-maintained problem behavior: Empirical support and clinical recommendations. *Journal of Evidence-Based Practices for Schools, 10*, 70–92.

Grenny, J., Patterson, K., McMillan, R., Switzler, A., & Gregory, E. (2022). *Crucial conversations: Tools for talking when stakes are high* (3rd ed.). McGraw Hill.

Heinicke, M. R., Juanico, J. F., Valentino, A. L., & Sellers, T. P. (in press). Improving behavior analysts' public speaking: Recommendations from expert interviews. *Behavior Analysis in Practice.*

Kristensen, T. S., Borritz, M., Villadsen, E., & Christensen, K. B. (2005). The copenhagen burnout inventory: A new tool for the assessment of burnout. *Work & Stress, 19*(3), 192-207.

Leach, D. J., Rogelberg, S. J., Warr, P. B., & Burnfield, J. L. (2009). Perceived meeting characteristics: The role of design characteristics. *Journal of Business Psychology, 24*, 65–76. https://doi.org/10.1007/s10869-009-9092-6.

LeBlanc, L. A., (2020). *Nobody's perfect.* Retrieved on April 3, 2020, from https://www.aubreydaniels.com/media-center/nobodys-perfect

LeBlanc, L. A., & Nosik, M. (2019). Planning and leading effective meetings. *Behavior Analysis in Practice, 12*, 696-708.

LeBlanc, L. A., Heinicke, M. R., & Baker, J. C. (2012). Expanding the consumer base for behavior-analytic services: Meeting the needs of consumers in the 21st century. *Behavior Analysis in Practice, 5*(1), 4-14.

LeBlanc, L. A., Sellers, T. P., & Ala'i, S. (2020). *Building and sustaining meaningful and effective relationships as a supervisor and mentor.* Sloan Publishing.

LeBlanc, L. A., Sleeper, J. D., Mueller, J. R., Jenkins, S. R., & Harper-Briggs, A. M. (2020). Assessing barriers to effective caseload management by practicing behavior analysts. *Journal of Organizational Behavior Management, 39*(3–4), 317–336.

LeBlanc, L. A., Taylor, B. A., & Marchese N. V. (2019). The training experiences of behavior analysts: Compassionate care and therapeutic relationships with caregivers. *Behavior Analysis in Practice, 13*, 387–393. https://doi.org/10.1007/s40617-019-00368-z

Miltenberger, R. G. (2015). *Behavior modification: Principles and procedures* (6th Edition). Cengage.

Murphy, S. E., & Ensher, E. A. (2001). The role of mentoring support and self-management strategies on reported career outcomes. *Journal of Career Development, 27*(4), 229–246.

Parsons, M. B., Rollyson, J. H., & Reid, D. H. (2012). Evidence-based staff training. *Behavior Analysis in Practice, 5*, 2–11. doi: 10.1007/BF03391819

Plantiveau, C., Dounavi, K., & Virués-Ortega, J. (2018). High levels of burnout among early career board-certified behavior analysts with low collegial support in the work environment. *European Journal of Behavior Analysis, 19*(2), 195-207.

Sellers, T. P., Alai-Rosales, S., & MacDonald, R. P. (2016). Taking full responsibility: The ethics of supervision in behavior analytic practice. *Behavior Analysis in Practice, 9*(4), 299-308.

Sellers, T. P., LeBlanc, L. A., & Valentino, A. L. (2016). Recommendations for detecting and addressing barriers to successful supervision. *Behavior Analysis in Practice, 9*(4), 309-319.

Sellers, T. P., Valentino, A. L., & LeBlanc, L. A. (2016). Recommended practices for individual supervision of aspiring behavior analysts. *Behavior Analysis in Practice, 9*(4), 274-286.

Skinner, B. F. (1953). *Science and human behavior.* Macmillan.

Skinner, B. F. (1957). *Verbal behavior.* Prentice Hall.

Skinner, B. F. (1968). *The technology of teaching.* Appleton-Century-Crofts

Taylor, B. A., LeBlanc, L. A., & Nosik, M. R. (2019). Compassionate care in behavior analytic treatment: Can outcomes be enhanced by attending to relationships with caregivers?. *Behavior Analysis in Practice, 12,* 654–666. https://doi.org/10.1007/s40617-018-0089-3

Turner, L. B., Fischer, A. J., & Luiselli, J. K. (2016). Towards a competency-based, ethical, and socially valid approach to the supervision of applied behavior analytic trainees. *Behavior Analysis in Practice, 9*(4), 287-298.

Ward-Horner, J., & Sturmey, P. (2012). Component analysis of behavior skills training in functional analysis. *Behavioral Interventions, 27*(2), 75–92.

Wenger, E. C., & Snyder, W. M. (2000). Communities of practice: The organizational frontier. *Harvard Business Review, 78*(1), 139–146.

Wright, P. I. (2019). Cultural humility in the practice of applied behavior analysis. *Behavior Analysis in Practice, 12,* 805–809.

ABA Technologies designs research-based learning solutions for every type of industry. As experts in behavior change and learning science, ABA Technologies helps transform organizations to build a culture of learning. They work with organizations to create a learning architecture that focuses on achieving sustainable practices. For over twenty-five years, ABA Technologies has solely focused on eLearning solutions and served 240,000+ individual learners in 60+ countries. They believe that "Learning can no longer occur in a vacuum. It needs to be infused into every part of the workplace to change performance and impact business results." ABA Technologies has the experience and agility to supercharge your learning program!

ABA Technologies, Inc. @abatechnologies @abatechnologies @aba_technologies ABA Technologies, Inc.

ABA Technologies, Inc. Brands

www.abatechnologies.com

Offering professional development programs for continuing education and career or personal growth is one way we support our mission and the field of behavior analysis. We offer a superior level of learner focus and instructional design, high-quality content from leading experts in the field, and an easy-to-use platform that allows for learning anytime and easy connections to other learners.

A Sample of ABA Tech Academy Courses:

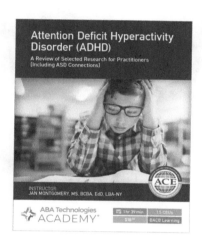

"I like the module/phase chunking of the course, the recordings, and the interactive question-answer practice. The instructors were enjoyable to listen to, professional, and knowledgeable. I loved Jose's comments at the end, and the tribute to Jose was beautifully done."

–Stacey, Verified student in the OBM Specialist Certificate course

www.ABATechAcademy.com

KeyPress Publishing

We strive to provide individualized services and support to all our authors. Our team of experts is here to answer all your questions and produce your ideal products. We offer personal attention from the time you reach out, through the writing, submission, and review process, close partnerships with our design team to fulfill your visions, and our publishing expertise to help you publish, promote, and sell your book.

A Sample of KeyPress Publications:

"The book KeyPress Publishing created for me is professional and beautiful, and we already have another book in process."

–Janis Allen, Owner of Performance Leadership Consulting

www.KeyPressPublishing.com

Register your book with KeyPress Publishing

Registered users receive exclusive reader benefits and stay connected with

- special discounts on books and ABA Tech Academy courses
- opportunities to preview new products, and
- subscription to ABA Technologies' monthly newsletter that delivers tools, tips, and articles focused on instructional design innovation, BACB ACE CEs, and professional development courses